Turf Accounts

TURF ACCOUNTS

A Connoisseur's Racing Anthology

Edited by

Gee Armytage and Mike Seabrook

GOLLANCZ/WITHERBY

LONDON

First published in Great Britain 1994
by Gollancz/Witherby
A Division of the Cassell group
Villiers House, 41/47 Strand, London WC2N 5JE

The Today *Horse* © John Timpson 1994
The Ringer © Michael Pope 1994
A Day in the Jockeys' Room © Robin Oakley 1994
Day In, Day Out © Geoff O'Hara 1994
Cartmel © John Budden 1994
How I Loved You © James Morton 1994
The Amateur © Simon Raven 1994
The Anglo-Russian Steeplechase Challenge 1990 © Reg Whitehead
A Horserace Made in Heaven © Tony Morris 1994
The Sport of . . . er . . . © Eamonn Percival 1994
The Hermit Affair © Michael Church 1994
A Day Out with Winlaw © Tim Heald 1994
A Season's Dreamin' © Gee Armytage 1994
'Tall Oaks from Little Acorns Grow' © Ian Wallace 1994
The Rise and Rise of My Uncle Ernie © David Benedictus 1994
Back to Basics © Julian Wilson 1994
First Past the Post © William Powell 1994
They All Hurt © Richard Pitman 1994
Tregonwell Frampton – Father of the Turf © Miles Napier 1994
The Ovaltinies © Mike Seabrook 1994
The Start of My Career © Peter Walwyn 1994
A Cautionary Tale © Paul Haigh 1994

A catalogue record for this book
is available from the British Library

ISBN 0 85493 246 1

Photoset by Rowland Phototypesetting Ltd
Bury St Edmunds, Suffolk, and printed in Great Britain by
St Edmundsbury Press Ltd, Bury St Edmunds, Suffolk

Contents

Introduction

MIKE SEABROOK

That the British are an odd people is such a truism that one almost feels bashful about saying it again; and nothing is odder about them than their mystifying capacity to combine in a single national character the prurient and the puritanical, the coarse and the exalted, the high and the lowest of the low. Our press, for example, presents simultaneous images of *The Times* severely intoning the news in pristine prose and refusing to get excited about it (a role rather taken over by the *Independent* in recent years), the *Guardian* solemnly reminding us of our moral imperatives, while all the time the papers at the yellow end of the spectrum are revelling cheerfully in tales of vicars and choirboys, film stars and Mars bars, hamsters and the robust thinking of the saloon bar at closing time.

Nothing demonstrates this split personality of the British more graphically than Anglo-Saxon attitudes to sport. Many years ago the journalists of *The Times* went on strike, and to help with their domestic finances they produced a spoof edition of their own paper. Among the most amusing pieces in it was an article bemoaning the current rise in croquet hooliganism. It raised a universal chuckle. Yet I have, on one of my few ventures into the abodes of the mighty, observed behaviour in a croquet match between a peer of the realm and a mild, greying country clergyman which, had it taken place in a boxing booth in Poplar, would have brought instant suspension, and probably a full-scale riot and the attentions of the local police as well.

It was said of old that proficiency at the game of snooker was the sign of a misspent youth; snooker went from that place beneath lofty and well-bred contempt to being the favourite televiewing of the nation. Another celebrated saw declares that football –

Association football that is – is a gentleman's game played by hooligans, while rugby is a hooligan's game played by gentlemen. That does have a grain of truth in it; but it signally fails to take account of the fact that it was rugby union that gave us the gentle art of biting ears off, and that things routinely go on in the scrum compared to which the professional foul, Jack Charlton's little black book and Vinny Jones and all his works would seem as moonlight unto sunlight, as water unto wine.

Nowhere is this duality more apparent than in our attitudes towards one of the most ancient sporting arts of all: the sport of kings, image of war without its guilt, the Turf – in a word, racing. Nowhere is the contrast starker between the elevated and the lowly, the refined and the louche: on the one side, the Queen and her mother, seemingly half of *Burke's Peerage* and a good deal of whatever the Arabian equivalent may be. On the other, shifty, blue-jowled characters sidling into Honest Sid's, fingering greasy tenners as they scan the pinned-up pages of the *Sporting Life* from beneath low foreheads and bony brows and prepare to plank the housekeeping on some animated bone-bag, whose villainous trainer was probably giving it a bucket of water just before the race at one end while the stable lad was injecting it with stimulants at the other, and whose jockey will probably pull it anyway, just in case. And somewhere in the middle there are sweetly spoken, gently bred boys (and girls): Steve Cauthen and Walter Swinburn, the Smith-Eccleses, Dunwoodys and Armytages; and always there, utterly *sui generis*, the housewives of England's perennial favourite and apparently scheduled to go on for ever, a man who could surely never have been anything but English, the Long Fellow, who I shouldn't mind betting nine-tenths of the nation would like to see become *Sir* Lester and the hell with his conviction; and, in between also, every typist and office boy in the land, and their boss, having their ten bob in the office sweep on the Derby and the National.

All these images are contradictory of the others; all are equally true. And that is why this sport, above all others, has such a universal appeal: there is room for everybody, and all racing folk have something to say, some point of contact, to the others. How odd this, and what rich paradox, that the one sport above all others which necessarily has only the rich at one end, in which well-bred accents are the rule in the middle, notoriously draws those of the very opposite strain to its nether edges, to make the sport of kings probably the most truly democratic sport of all.

Just as all these apparently strange bedfellows co-exist happily in racing itself, so they sit comfortably beside each other between the covers of this celebration of the sport – united by the twin common factors of a profound affection for the people, the animals, the places, the ambience of the sport, and the ability to write about it with fluency, feeling and style.

Some of our contributors are, or have been, active participants in this difficult, dangerous sport. Richard Pitman writes very amusingly about his days of, as he puts it, galloping on and bouncing off the turf, with a nonchalance that makes light of the very real, and fearsome, dangers to which jockeys cheerfully expose themselves. My co-editor Gee Armytage takes us through a season's hopes, rewards and disappointments in the pursuit of her great dream, of winning – and becoming the first of her sex to win – The Big One, the race in which those dangers are at their most real and, to be sure, their most fearsome, the Grand National. The trainers of today are represented by Peter Walwyn, who tells of his lifelong love affair with horses and racing them, while the previous generation has a genial and very funny spokesman in Michael Pope. His tale of a very naughty affair reminds us of the less reputable side of the sport, but it reminds us also of his inimitably sunny, genial approach to it, which was summed up by the title of his first book of his reminiscences, *All Such Fun*.

That would strike a resounding chime of sympathy in the breast of Julian Wilson: he has been a successful owner of racehorses, but is best known, of course, as one of the household names and faces of racing commentary. He utters a *cri de coeur* for the more elegant and relaxed atmosphere of racing a few decades ago. Two of our other contributors, however, take us a lot farther back than that: Miles Napier, another of our team who has been involved in racing all his life, gives us a fascinating portrait of one of the greatest characters in all the history of a sport notably rich in 'characters'; and Michael Church tells of a racing rivalry that spilled over into other areas of its participants' lives. Both show in passing that the rough, tough side of racing is nothing at all new. Tony Morris too delves into racing's rich history, but also comes right up to date, to indulge in the eternal pleasure of speculation: which was the best ever? His horserace made in Heaven offers much food for debate, and everyone will have a different idea of the order of finishing.

Other forms of racing life and other forms of literature are not neglected, either. They coalesce in a tale by Geoff O'Hara, himself a bookie for thirty years, of a likable bookie and his somewhat less than reputable friends and customers in a not altogether respectable part of London. Geoff O'Hara's story deals with the low life of racing. Eamonn Percival, who also offers short fiction, deals with lower life still. His account of a day at the races with readers of the *Sun* is witty and sometimes hilarious. If Messrs O'Hara and Percival tell of low life, our seventh short story deals with the after-life: Simon Raven has had a lifelong fascination with both the Turf and the ghost story. Here, in the setting of his favourite British racecourse, he gives us an example of the genre that will make your flesh crawl.

The supernatural – or at any rate, the paranormal – is also involved in James Morton's account of his great love affair with the Turf, and with his own horse.

Simon Raven's old friend John Budden, who features regularly in his volumes of memoirs, is not only a regular racing writer, commentator and punter, but also has the good fortune to live not far from Cartmel, one of the remotest and most atmospheric of all Britain's courses. He writes of its charms and of its drawbacks and, as a bonus, tells the story of the most audacious and memorable swindle in recent racing history: the Gay Future affair.

Coming thus right up to the present, we accompany Tim Heald on a day at Chepstow with another of the colourful characters with which racing abounds; enjoy a day in the normally out of bounds region of the jockeys' weighing room with Robin Oakley; and share in a disastrous weekend's financial misadventures with Paul Haigh in Ireland. We follow Ian Wallace's long fascination for the sport, from his single, disastrous foray into bookmaking to his leisurely appreciation of Newmarket today; and we share the solitary, but ecstatic moment of triumph for once-only part-owner John Timpson in his hilarious account of the short career of a horse called Today.

Finally, we wander off into some odd and unexpected corners of the racing world: William Powell MP, gives us an interesting glimpse into the mysterious world and the arcane rituals of the

House of Commons, with some revealing insights into party betting habits and many fascinating miscellaneous oddments of information; David Benedictus tells the amusing story of the system he invented for winning money off bookmakers; and Reg Whitehead takes us farther afield by a long distance than anyone else, to Pyatigorsk and sundry other remote regions of Russia, establishing friendly racing relations even before those of the diplomatic kind had thawed out.

The collection is completed by myself, reminiscing about the time some ten years ago when I regularly ran with a crowd of racing men. Looking back, I always seemed to have more money in those days than I ever seem to have now, and I'm damned sure I had less sense; but I miss those days, and the old gang I used to knock about with, almost more than I can say. Writing about them for this book brought with it an almost unbearable feeling of time passing, and of loss. As a strictly private thing, therefore, I'm dedicating my part of this book, with great affection, to them: to John Marshall; to Bill Ball; and to Ted Pearce, Jim Hammond, Charlie Lloyd, Tug Wilson, and all the rest of the gang, wherever they may be.

The Today Horse

JOHN TIMPSON

It was Ian Robertson who suggested it. Ian is a BBC rugby commentator and in his day was no mean player himself, but his sporting interests extended to the race track as well as the football field, and he had already formed a syndicate among his sportsroom colleagues to buy a horse called Rugby Special, which had actually won the odd race.

'Why doesn't the *Today* team buy a horse?' he asked casually over breakfast, after the programme had ended. Robert Robinson looked at me, I looked at Robert, and we both looked skyward.

'Be so good as to pass the cornflake packet,' said Robert. And that might have been that.

Also having breakfast, however, was Marshall Stewart, at that time editor of *Today* and a journalist with a nose for publicity. 'A *Today* horse,' he murmured. 'Tell us more.'

It may seem an unlikely setting for what we originally regarded as a dotty idea but which built up, as breakfast progressed, into the makings of the Racing Coup of the Century. *Today* breakfasts had changed considerably in style and content since the plush days of the 1960s, when Jack de Manio and his guests adjourned to a BBC hospitality suite to enjoy a quite handsome spread, served on a real dining table and using proper cutlery and plates with the BBC crest. In the 1970s breakfast arrived on a BBC trolley in the poky little anteroom next to the *Today* office: a carton of orange juice, miniature packets of cornflakes or muesli, and a pile of soggy toast.

(We constantly pleaded for a toastrack to preserve a faint element of crispness, but the only crisp result was the reply from the Catering Manager. She said if she provided a toastrack it would only get stolen – and I am afraid she was probably right. That was why we were also condemned to plastic spoons and paper cups.)

There was however an added ingredient in those days which may have encouraged our growing enthusiasm for Ian's proposal. Each morning, from whence I know not, and I never asked, a bottle of whisky materialized in the midst of the cornflakes and the soggy toast.

This was not as depraved or decadent as it may seem, though I doubt if Lord Reith would approve. The overnight staff were going off duty after a twelve- or fifteen-hour shift, and this was in the nature of a nightcap before they went home to bed. For the early morning shift and the presenters, who had been working four or five hours, breakfast was at lunchtime, and an aperitif was not out of place. And our guests, who may have just experienced their first live interview on a programme listened to by millions, were often grateful for a glass, either to celebrate their triumph or to forget their discomfiture.

The practice, for various reasons, has long since died out, and Lord Reith can rest in peace, but that morning the usual bottle was on the trolley, and it had just been opened when Ian suggested we buy a horse. By the time he had explained what was involved and what might be achieved, the bottle was half-empty and the idea did not seem so dotty after all. By the time the bottle was finished, the *Today* syndicate had been born.

Horse-owning syndicates are quite common now, but in 1973 they were still something of a novelty. The Jockey Club had only permitted them for four years, and their spokesman was not enthusiastic. 'Members of syndicates are in it for the fun and not the money – or at any rate they should be. Few syndicates ever show a profit.'

We had not heard that warning, but I doubt if it would have stopped us. We were in it, not only for the fun, but for the publicity. A syndicate linked with a popular radio programme and featuring three or four well-known names could hardly fail to win a headline, even if it failed to win a race. As it turned out, we won both.

A few early decisions were made. The horse would naturally be called Today. We devised special breakfast-time colours of burnt-toast brown, marmalade orange and tomato juice red. The syndicate would consist of twelve members and friends of the *Today* staff, nominally headed by Robert Robinson and myself, but with Ian as technical adviser and Marshall handling the publicity. Each member would contribute £100 to the initial cost of acquiring the horse, and ten pounds a month for its upkeep.

The figures seem small these days, but we were not expecting to win the Derby – not first time out, anyway – and we did in fact finish up with quite a small horse. Ian bought it through his racing contacts for a modest eight hundred guineas, and arranged for it to join the string (as I learned to say) of a very reputable trainer, Richard Hannon. One chilly day in December we all went down to his stables in Wiltshire – accompanied by a photographer, of course – to makes its acquaintance.

The scene was just as I had pictured it, a long line of horses' heads sticking out of a long line of stable doors. When we appeared at the entrance all the heads turned towards us – except one. The horse at the far end of the line had his teeth firmly clamped around the bottom half of the door.

'He quite likes chewing his door,' said Mr Hannon, perhaps a shade too nonchalantly.

'Any particular reason?' asked Robert.

'He hasn't told us yet,' said Mr Hannon, his Irish origin beginning to show. 'But don't worry. He lets go of the door at feed time.'

This, I felt, was my moment, and I produced the lump of sugar which I had acquired from the breakfast trolley. I held it out invitingly. The horse raised its eyes briefly to look at it, then turned its attention back to the door. Its teeth remained firmly embedded.

'It takes a little more than a lump of sugar,' Mr Hannon explained politely. 'Why don't you all go out to the paddock and we'll follow.'

We obediently went out to the paddock. I did glance back to see if he was using a crowbar on those teeth, but he was merely fetching a bucket. Sure enough, in due course, a stable lad rode Today into the paddock.

I have mentioned that it was quite a small horse. I have been looking at the group photograph again, and I have to say it was a very small horse indeed. Robert Robinson is a medium-sized man, but in the photograph the top of his head is level with Today's ears. I am a few inches taller, and I appear to be looming over them both. The stable lad's feet seem to be within inches of the ground.

'He's a twin,' Ian explained. 'Twins are always smaller. But he's got a very good background – he was sired by Jimmy Reppin.' It sounded as though Today ought to be a centaur, but Jimmy Reppin, it transpired, was a horse too, and quite a successful one at that.

Robert was not convinced. 'If all else fails,' he said, 'we can always enter him for the Greyhound Derby . . .'

Some three months and thirty pounds a head later, Today was pronounced ready for his first race. Ian Robertson, Richard Hannon and their various advisers decided that he should make his debut in the 4.30 at Leicester, the Atalanta Plate. The going, it seemed, would be ideal for small horses which liked chewing doors.

To our gratification, the racing writers seemed to agree. One of them noted that another runner in this race, trained by ex-jockey Duncan Keith, was also making its debut and was expected to go well, 'but a better bet may be Today, a well-bred son of the smart Jimmy Reppin'. The headline over the story announced firmly: 'Today to Upset Keith.'

At about 4.33 that afternoon it became apparent that some racing journalists know just about as much about racing as we did. The well-bred son failed to be as smart as his father, and came fourth. The headline, however, may have been correct. Keith's horse was unplaced, and it must have been upsetting for an ex-jockey trainer to see his horse beaten by a very amateur racing syndicate.

Richard Hannon was not at all discouraged. Fourth place, he assured us, was very creditable first time out, albeit unrewarding. He would try him at Kempton Park on Easter Saturday – and this time, why didn't Robert and I come along too?

It was a tempting thought. Saturday was our day off, Kempton Park was within reasonable range, and we had yet to experience the delights of the owners' enclosure. On top of which, the sports editor said it would be a rather jolly wheeze if we did the running commentary on the race . . .

I still have my owner's badge pasted into my scrapbook. It is just a humble piece of pink cardboard with a hole in it, but when attached to a blue piece of cardboard saying 'Club Enclosure', and hung nonchalantly from the lapel, it is a passport to privilege. Happily there is nothing on it to reveal I was merely a one-twelfth owner, though the racecard did name Mr Robert Robinson as the sole proprietor – only because of alphabetical order, I was assured. The other owners may not have noticed that, however, and I rubbed shoulders proudly with latter-day Lord Roseberys, and talked knowledgeably to men in curly-brimmed brown felt hats about the goodness of the going.

It was during one of these conversations that I felt a tug at my jacket. I looked round, then looked down. A very small man in a long macintosh and riding breeches was trying to attract my attention.

'Excuse me,' he said. 'I'm Durr.'

The name, if it was a name, meant nothing.

'Ah,' I said.

'I've come for your instructions,' said the very small man.

It sounded like a line from a Mafia film. The words, 'Waste him, Durr,' sprang to mind. Richard Hannon came to the rescue.

'This is Frankie Durr,' he explained. 'He's our jockey.'

I looked suitably impressed. Frankie Durr, on the other hand, did not look impressed at all. But he had ridden for a lot of owners, and I suppose we were no dafter than most.

'I'm riding Today,' he observed, and I had the terrible urge to reply: 'Well, so long as you finish today . . .' But fortunately Mr Durr kept talking. 'How would you like me to ride him, sir?'

I was at a loss. 'Well, Mr Durr,' I said vaguely, 'I would say, ride him to win.'

This time it was his turn to say: 'Ah.' He exchanged a glance with Richard Hannon, who bravely maintained a straight face, then turned to leave. But as he did so he remembered another query, and turned back.

'Do you think,' he asked, 'that you could get me Robert Robinson's autograph?'

It was at this point that Today came into the ring, saving me from making the icy response I was planning. He was easily spotted, because he was by far the smallest horse in the line. I glanced again at Frankie Durr, and reminded myself that he in his turn was a very small man . . .

Robert and I were ushered into the commentary box to describe to the nation the excitements and dramas of the 4.55 at Kempton. It was called the Waterloo Stakes, and the title proved appropriate, because if I ever harboured hopes of being a racing commentator, this was where I met my Waterloo. My efforts were not quite in the same category as Tommy Woodruffe's commentary on the Royal Naval Review – the Fleet, you may recall, was 'all lit up', and Commander Woodruffe was glowing a bit too – but I think that Robert and I demonstrated very clearly that race-commentating is a highly specialized art.

The race was only five furlongs, and it is surprising how quickly even a small horse can cover five furlongs. We had barely cried: 'They're off!' before they were into the final furlong.

'Here they come!' I remember yelling.

'So they do,' observed Robert, more sedately.

And as they came, I realized that the diminutive figure of Today was actually near the front.

'Come on, Today!' I roared, regardless of the BBC's reputation for unbiased reporting. Even Robert was moved to murmur, quite audibly: 'Yes, do come on, old chap.'

Today did his best to oblige, and Mr Durr stood up in the stirrups in a quite dramatic fashion, waving his whip and uttering strange cries. But it was not to be. A much larger horse drew ahead by a length and a half, and little Today finished up with the sympathy vote and second place.

Robert and I were commiserating with each other when the producer nudged us rather heavily. 'If you wouldn't mind,' he said, 'I think the listeners might be quite interested to know who's won.'

I was torn between 'How do I know?' and 'Who cares?' but he handed us the result. The winner turned out to be Some Treasure, at odds of five to one. The odds on Today were nine to two, which as I understand it meant that it should have narrowly beaten Some Treasure. But then the favourite came nowhere, so who really knows anything about anything?

I was tempted to say all this to the listeners, but racing enthusiasts like to preserve their illusions, and by now I was almost a racing enthusiast myself. So I read the results, in as deadpan a voice as I could muster, though I was told later that there was a wealth of bitterness in my rendering of Some Treasure.

We met Mr Durr briefly after the weigh-in. 'Bad luck,' I said magnanimously. He just nodded. Doubtless he was already thinking about his next race, and the next idiot he had to contend with in the owners' enclosure.

I was not entirely despondent. My each-way bet on the Tote had produced a modest but encouraging thirty-one pence, and I was visualizing better things to come. Richard Hannon too was optimistic.

'He's coming good,' he assured us. 'I'll enter him at Epsom on April 23rd.'

'Great!' I said. 'We'll be there.'

Then we remembered. The twenty-third of April was the day of the Radio Industries Club awards ceremony at the Connaught Rooms, and not only had Robert Robinson been named Radio Personality of the Year, but the *Today* programme had won the award for Radio Programme of the Year, for the third successive time. There was no avoiding it; we had to be there.

On the morning of the 23rd we scanned the racing pages avidly. Today was entered in the 2 p.m. race, the Cuddington Stakes, and the little chap was quoted as favourite at two to one. The opposition did not look too strong; I had discovered by now what the little numbers meant in front of the horses' names, and while Today had achieved a second place, the best place the others could muster between them was a third. All the rest had a succession of noughts.

Reading the very small print, I discovered that one horse, ambiguously named Another Faerie, had been in the same race as Today at Kempton Park, but only finished sixth. Our jockey, I noted, was again the diminutive Mr Durr; maybe he and Today were forging a famous partnership; all the omens looked good, but alas, we would not be at Epsom to cheer them on.

By this stage in our racing career we had established an account with a friendly neighbourhood bookie, who provided a telephoned race commentary for his clients – and this was to be our salvation. Just before two o'clock, as coffee was being served in the Connaught Rooms, I sneaked out of the hall and installed myself in the phone box by the gentlemen's cloakroom, armed with a great pile of small change.

As it turned out, I needed it all. The race itself, another five-furlong dash, was over during the first two-pennyworth, and the commentary was so rapid I hardly caught a word, but the vital information at the end of it was clear enough: there was a photo-finish, and one of the horses was Today.

I sat, spellbound, in the phone box, feeding in coin after coin as I waited for the result, while a restive queue built up outside. When the man at the front started tapping on the glass I opened the door to explain.

'It's a photo-finish,' I told him. 'The *Today* horse. It's in a photo-finish. At Epsom.'

Miraculously, he had heard of the *Today* horse; the publicity had not been in vain. 'Splendid,' he said, and passed on the news. The rest of the queue gathered round. All thoughts of the radio awards had disappeared.

My change was nearly exhausted and I was about to have a whip-round, when the news came through. 'The result of the two o'clock at Epsom,' came the expressionless voice. 'First, Today, trained by Richard Hannon, ridden by . . .'

'We've done it!' I cried, throwing the remaining coins into the air, and the queue actually cheered. Hands reached out to grasp mine, others thumped my back, faces beamed. The popularity of the *Today* programme was the main reason, of course – and they were also now able to use the phone – but that moment outside the gentlemen's cloakroom at the Connaught Rooms was the high spot of my racing career.

The award ceremony itself was almost an anticlimax. I would have liked to stand on the table and shout: 'We've won!' but that is not the way you are expected to behave at an award ceremony, even when you are referring to a horse race and not the actual award. I am told, however, that my face when I re-entered the hall was a sight to behold . . .

The financial benefits from Today's win at Epsom were not dramatic. The prize money was £562, which covered his board and lodging for the next few months, and my three-pound bet produced enough to buy him an extra bag of oats. In racing terms it was peanuts, but to the *Today* syndicate it was the start of a glorious future. Or so we thought.

As the season progressed, Today revealed a disturbing new side to his personality. His affinity for stable doors had been brought under control, and he never actually appeared on the track with a door still clamped in his teeth, but it became apparent that he had a phobia about turning corners. His first races were all in a straight line, but when he was faced with a bend in the track he just kept going, no matter how hard Mr Durr or his successors tried to dissuade him. He had five more races, but he never got in the frame again, as we racing folk say. After the October meeting at Doncaster, when he was again unplaced, we decided that *Today* would call it a day.

There had been other developments that summer anyway. Robert Robinson was calling it a day too – 'These early mornings are turning me into a zombie' – and as he was the nominal owner of the horse, the venture rather lost its point. Marshall Stewart too had left, to be editor of the new LBC commercial radio station. Rather sadly, the syndicate decided to disband, and Today was put up for sale.

He was bought by some optimist in Singapore for a thousand pounds, a figure which left us substantially out of pocket overall, but we felt more sorry for the little horse than for ourselves. Singapore, after all, is quite a small island, and with his propensity for only running in straight lines, I fear he probably ended up in the sea. I would have preferred to put him out to grass, with a good supply of stable doors to keep him happy.

As for the remaining members of the syndicate, our racing days were over. It was all a bit of a giggle while it lasted, and judging by the cuttings the public enjoyed it too. Certainly I still treasure the memory of that scene outside the gents at the Connaught Rooms. But our little adventure confirmed what every racing man knows; there is only one quicker way of losing money than betting on horses, and that is to own one . . .

The Ringer

MICHAEL POPE

There was a period back in the late 1940s when I was very short of horses to train. After badgering my owners to let me go shopping on their behalf I set off for the December sales at Newmarket with orders for a couple of rising three year olds for the flat, a potential hurdler and an older horse with sufficient scope to jump fences another day.

When I examined the catalogue the name Pelican Pete kept haunting me. I couldn't think why, but when I checked the form book I remembered: he was, of course, the brute that had beaten my filly Wandering Annie in suspicious circumstances in a moderate event for two year olds at Alexandra Park earlier in the season.

I had thought our filly was a certainty on all known form, and her owner, Randall Knight, and I had bet like drunken sailors. On the race card the trainer of the eventual winner was given as Ted Dill, a crafty looking little runt whom I had never seen before and have never seen since.

He had appeared very agitated after the race and told his lad to take the horse back to the stables and get off home as soon as he could. We thought this rather odd, but it was none of our business. We'd done our dough and that was that.

No doubt I would have forgotten the episode if the name Pelican Pete had not appeared in the sales catalogue some three and a half months later, as 'Lot 198 chesnut colt by William Tell out of Peter's Sister'. He was stabled down the town in a small yard near the Clock Tower. Curiosity told me that I ought to take a quick look at him.

A scruffy looking lad was squatting on an upturned wooden bucket outside the box door with a butt-end, long gone out, stuck on his bottom lip. I recognized him immediately as the lad who had led the horse up at Alexandra Park. That wasn't difficult: he had long, scruffy ginger hair with a large, unsightly purple wart like a birthmark on the side of his nose.

Peering over the stable door it struck me that the animal tugging away at a near-empty hay-net was a much smaller individual than the one that had beaten Wandering Annie, but maybe he would look bigger out of his box, as so many horses do. I signalled the lad to pop a bridle on and pull him out.

Fair enough: he was the same colour, a liver chesnut, and similar in other respects, but even so I just knew he was not the same animal. I said to the lad, 'Were you looking after this fellow when he won at Ally Pally away back in the summer?' Flushing up like mad he stammered, 'No, guv, I've only been with Mr Dill a couple of weeks.' Of course he was lying through his teeth, which confirmed that all was not on the level. I now had a strong feeling that the horse which beat us must have been a ringer.

As I was pondering whether I should report my suspicions, two fellows armed with photographic gear started clicking away like Japanese tourists without so much as a 'by your leave' either to the lad or myself.

They continued to take picture after picture from every angle, close up, from afar, standing still, on the move, of his head, knees, joints, hocks, feet and tail. In fact I thought any minute they would cock his tail and take a snap of his anus.

I asked, 'Why are you taking all these photographs, and have you permission to do so?' to which one of them replied in an authoritative tone as he flashed his identity badge, 'On instructions of the Metropolitan Police.' Further evidence that my suspicions were justified and that I had not just been reading too much Nat Gould.

When I arrived back up at the Park Paddocks the first person I saw was my great chum Frank Cundell. He was chatting away in earnest to another neighbouring trainer John Goldsmith and his wife Tiny. Frank said, 'Hey! come here Mike, you're just the fellow I want to see, and have I got some gossip for you? Old Nosey Farquar, who was my buddy in Cairo during the war, is now boss of the Jockey Club Security Team, has just whispered to me in strict confidence that he is here to further his investigations into a case of suspected ringing.'

Frank continued. 'I knew you'd be interested because one of the horses thought to be involved is Pelican Pete, coming up for sale a few Lots later. Surely that's the brute that did us out of our dough at Ally Pally when you thought Wandering Annie was a good thing back in the summer.' At that moment an announcement boomed over the tannoy. 'Lot 198, Pelican Pete, has been withdrawn by order of the Metropolitan Police.'

A few days later the bubble really burst and the Stewards of the Jockey Club could no longer keep their suspicions from the press. They really went to town and started piecing the case together with hungry journalists crawling everywhere.

It eventually transpired that Dave Murray, hitherto a respected owner with a number of horses trained at Epsom, had decided to apply for permission to train privately. He had rented a small yard behind the Perch and Pike in Mewsy near Wantage and had employed a dubious little Irishman called Ted Dill to hold the licence. Apparently he had held a similar post at the Northolt ponies but had left under a cloud, and in something of a hurry.

Dave Murray and his brother Jack were fearsome gamblers and renowned for having a crack at the ring. Once installed Dill was instructed to go to Ireland and search for a three year old with decent winning form. Eventually he found the very article, belonging to an old acquaintance of his called Paddy Burns. The horse was a liver chesnut called Copper Knob, with no distinctive markings other than a small white star on his forehead.

Paddy was skint and unable to run his colt, which had won two quite useful races earlier in the season, because he was on the forfeit list. However, a bulging roll of white fivers with a promise of a lot more to come soon persuaded Paddy to lease the horse for twelve months with no questions asked.

Dill's next task was to find a two year old as like Copper Knob as possible, preferably with little or no form to his credit. One wet Monday at Ascot Sales Dill spotted the very animal, an extremely moderate two year old called Pelican Pete that had run a number of times but had never been placed. He was the same colour as Copper Knob with similar markings except that he did not have any white about him.

However, Dill sensed he would be able to disguise the white star on Copper Knob with a strong dye. The two horses would then pass in a crowd as twins.

During the next few weeks Dave conjured up the final details for one of the most daring betting coups of recent times, the plan being for the moderate two-year-old Pelican Pete to be entered in a poor maiden at starting, and then for Copper Knob, the useful three year old, to be substituted for the younger horse and run under his name.

So far so good: all arrangements for the big day were in hand and the venue eventually chosen for the dirty deed was Alexandra Park. Little was I aware that in all innocence I would become even remotely involved with such a criminal act, but by sheer chance I had chosen the very same race to loose off Wandering Annie. She was quite useful, having been placed second three times, and on any known form was a good thing to collect. I duly suggested to Randall Knight the owner that we should have an old-fashioned punt.

To our utter amazement she was beaten half a length with ease by Pelican Pete, who had been heavily backed in spite of his poor record, his jockey sitting up like a policeman, trying not to win too far, while Wandering Annie had done her best but appeared not to be good enough. I turned to Randall and said, 'They must have been cheating with that bugger all season and stuffed him full of steroids as well, I shouldn't wonder.' Half jokingly I added, 'Unless of course he's a bloody ringer.'

Apparently the attempt to blot out the white star with dye had failed, so the local saddler had been employed to make a leather medallion to hang down from the brow-band and cover it up. Should by any chance any nosey devil enquire what purpose this article served the prearranged answer was to be that 'it's the owner's lucky mascot'.

An astute little cockney known as Bandy, who handled a number of betting operations for the wide boys in those days, was to be asked to handle the commission. Only recently, when I traced old Bandy down to a retirement home in Hove, he recalled some very amusing tales concerning the exciting event which took place so many years ago.

'I was doing a job up at Lanark for a couple of bent jockeys,' he said, 'when a telegram came through to the weighing room for me.

It said "Meet me Bald Faced Stag Ally Pally noon tomorrow. Going for the bacon. Fly down if need be. Signed Dave Murray."

'Blimey,' I thought to myself. 'I've never been off the bleedin' ground in me effing life and I'm buggered if I'll sprout wings now just to punt on a bleedin' 'orse!' However, he was a reliable little guy and wouldn't let you down, especially if he knew the lolly was right. He travelled down south all through the night using every manner of transport available and cast up at the Stag by taxi right on time.

There in the bar were Dave Murray, Ted Dill and a boss-eyed little geezer introduced merely as Paddy, who was apparently over from Ireland and shacked up with Dill for a week or two.

Dave, for whom Bandy had done business successfully in the past, did all the talking. 'We've got a certainty in the seller today and that's all you need know.' He continued, 'I want you to put me five grand on in the ring as late as possible. There'll be no other money for the horse because on paper his form is putrid. Meanwhile I'll chuck away a few hundred on the favourite Wandering Annie when the market opens with Ladbroke's, Hills, Beresfords and the others as a smoke screen.'

Bandy asked, 'What's in it for me? I've been travellin' all bleedin' night and need a decent cut – win or lose.'

Dave replied, 'Don't worry your devious little head about losing, this'll win all right and you'll cop two grand in readies with all the whisky you can pour down your scrawny little neck.'

The betting operation went well, Bandy struck his first bet at 100/8 and the last just before the 'off' at 100/30. He had averaged 7/1 to the total wager, in spite of the fact that the S.P. return was only 9/4. Mopping his brow, Bandy thought to himself, 'If this bugger collects they'll cop a bleedin' fortune.'

Dave had made himself scarce having instructed Dill to give the orders to the jockey, which were, 'This horse has come on two stone and won't get beat today. Have him up with the pace all the way and do just enough to win, but on no account win too far.'

Win! The horse was never off the bridle and won pulling a cart by a cheeky half-length with his head in his chest from Wandering Annie, who had given her all. With more rein and a kick in the belly the winner could have won by five lengths or even further.

It appeared that the perfect crime had been carried out with great skill and cunning. Dave warned Dill to lie low for a while and make sure that Paddy and Ginger did the same and kept off the bottle.

All was well for a while but one evening when downing a glass of bubbly at Eileen's Club in Jermyn Street, a well-known meeting place for the racing fraternity, Percy Thompson, the bookmaker, had a word in Dave's ear. 'A dickie bird tells me that the Jockey Club and the police have been tipped off to make a few discreet enquiries about your winner at Ally Pally back in the summer. I thought you should have your card marked!'

Dave immediately sent for Dill and told him that Copper Knob, the ringer, must be disposed of immediately without trace. At the same time Pelican Pete must be put back in his original box to satisfy any interlopers who might come ferreting about the yard.

After dark the very next night Ginger rode Copper Knob bare back up on to the Downs above the village. There on Lowberry Hill, Dill shot him between the eyes with his revolver. Old Bill, the gallop man, had dug a large hole with a digger on the front of his tractor, which then shovelled the poor horse into the grave before filling the dirt back and levelling over.

By now Dill, Ginger, Paddy and Bill were in a very dodgy state and called into the Perch and Pike for a few stiffeners to steady their nerves. When they were half pissed in came a young man who got into conversation and insisted on standing them a couple more rounds.

Unfortunately this young fellow was a plain-clothes detective and by closing time he had gleaned all the information he needed. Early next morning as the local trainers wended their way up to the Downs with their string of horses they spotted two large police Land-rovers parked on the side of the Ridgeway with four blokes digging for all they were worth by the open ditch on the schooling ground.

Sadly this was the finale to the Copper Knob and Pelican Pete drama – a well-laid plan that had so very nearly succeeded and frankly I am certain deep down most racing folk wished that it had. Dave Murray, Ted Dill and Paddy Burns were all found guilty and warned off the Turf for life, whilst Ginger admitted aiding and abetting, but he wasn't charged because on the eve of the trial he was knocked down and killed as he staggered legless out of the pub.

They do say the 'lucky' medallion, used to conceal the white star on Copper Knob, hangs over the bar in the Perch and Pike to this very day, mere mention of which sets Old Bill rambling on about the gripping case. The old boy is now rising ninety-three years of age, without a tooth in his head and stone deaf, but still enjoys his pint of old and mild. For the price of another half and a chaser they do say he'll show you where he dug the grave that very nearly concealed the vital evidence needed to prove the case.

To conclude this intriguing episode, when Wandering Annie had run her last race, Randall Knight sent her to the paddocks. Having been covered time and again by two different stallions plus the teaser as well, she remained barren, and an eminent veterinary surgeon reported that she would never conceive as long as she lived. In view of this I suggested to Randall that he should give her away to a good home, so off she went down to a friend of mine, David Hurn, who lived on Dartmoor and was certain to look after her well.

Under her new master she spent no less than fifteen seasons hunting at the head of the field with the Mid-Devon hounds over stone walls and across the wild terrain of the moor, only once giving her pilot a fall and never missing a day through lameness or ill health. When David decided she'd had enough, the mare was covered by the local stallion Sir Patrick, more for her own pleasure than anything else.

Believe it or not she proved to be in foal and produced a good-looking youngster. The following season, an encore, the second foal being by Ben Ross. Finally, when she had reached the age of twenty-nine, David decided with much sadness to put her down. She was buried in her own paddock, where away in the distance the horn blowing hounds for home can still be heard at the end of another hunt across the moor.

Whereas poor Copper Knob was not so lucky. At an early age he too had a burial, but not for the same reason and without a sporting family like the Hurns to remember him with love, respect and gratitude.

A Day in the Jockeys' Room

ROBIN OAKLEY

Out on Newbury's true galloping course it's a typical grey, cold winter racing day. Wind whips a loose page from somebody's *Sporting Life* up into the stands. Rain is threatening. On the steps of the weighing room lurk the interceptors, comfortably padded men in well-cut coats: owners, agents, racing journalists. A TV crew prowls in search of interviewees as trainers and travelling head lads pop into the office to sign up and declare their runners, some of them bantering to cadge an extra free race-card for a companion.

Inside, behind the sit-on weighing machine and a table covered with a green baize cloth, sits Derek Blake, Clerk of the Scales, checking the paperwork on today's runners. To one side is the stewards' room where adjudications will be made and instant justice dispensed if a jockey overuses his whip, steers the wrong course or comes back to scales after a race more than a pound lighter or more than two pounds heavier. (In the summer at least jockeys can easily sweat off a pound during a race. In the winter wet and muddy breeches and silks often come back heavier.) Derek will be watching for the dodges, like jockeys who weigh out with a lightweight pair of 'cheating boots' no heavier than ladies' slippers and then try to ride in something heavier. One of the attendant officials recalls how flat jockey Billy Newnes was warned one day that he must wear the 'passing boots' in which he'd weighed out. He did, but walked crablike back into the weighing room afterwards, apparently nearly crippled. For comfort he'd tucked torn up race-cards inside the thin boots. But it had been wet and the staples had soaked through the paper and become embedded in his feet, a result which earned him the nickname 'Staples' for some time after.

Around are weathered figures with outdoor faces wise in the ways of the world, the officials who hand out the number cloths, call the riders to the parade ring for mounting or check to see that girl-friends, hangers-on and even trainers don't penetrate behind into the jockeys' changing room. With a number of military men still involved at the top (Newbury's go-ahead chief executive, for example, is Major General David Pank, formerly the commander of British forces in Northern Ireland) there's plenty of deference left in racing. When in doubt people still tend to call you 'sir' just in case you're related to one of the stewards.

Through the snack bar and into the jockeys' changing room you move into a more informal world. It's early yet, with only a trickle of jockeys loping in barrel bags slung over their shoulders containing their saddles, safety helmets and compulsory spine protectors. In one corner lies a well-known rider, who shall be nameless for the sake of his relationship with trainer and owner, who's sleeping off the effects of the 'flu which has dogged him for two days, his head on a heap of towels. A lean white body, shoulders sticking out like coat-hangers from the emaciated frame, every bone visible, emerges from the shower room, complaining that the sauna hasn't been turned on. It's Mark Perrett, riding today for Martin Pipe. He carries eleven stone ten pounds in the third race, his only ride, but this is a man ever in quest of another half pound shed keeping himself lean enough to ride more than two stone lighter than that on the Flat.

Here in the jockeys' room the men who literally keep the show on the road are the valets. Midlands-based Tom Buckingham has been a valet for twenty-one years, sharing the business of looking after the needs of 150 jockeys with two assistants and his brother John, always remembered as the rider of the 1967 Grand National winner Foinavon, who triumphed after staying on his feet at the shambles of the twenty-third fence when almost every other runner was brought down. Dynasties are rife in racing and Pat Taylor, another leading valet, has done forty years in the job after his father did fifty-three before him.

There's the gentle scuffing of brush on boot, the slap of saddle soap on well-worn leather as they spruce up the kit. On the pegs around the room they've hung the breeches, sweatshirts, socks, tights, neck scarves and other items which the jockeys find waiting for them at every course in the land. On the table in the centre of the room, beside another huge set of step-on scales, they have piled the heaps of weights, flattened-out lead pancakes weighing around a pound apiece, which will be slipped into saddle cloths to adjust the burdens that horses carry to the handicapper's allotment, where the jockey's natural weight is less.

The other valets, blue aprons decked with the vital supplies of safety pins for securing loose breeches or tying up colours, are playing cards in the lull before the storm, praying it won't be one of those wet days which can make their lives a misery with demands for changes of breeches and some rapid tumble drying between races. Like theatrical dressers, valets can be father confessors and talismans, offering psychology along with the safety pins. Some jockeys like the same valet always to do up the ties on the caps of their racing silks. And they tend to hear the stories and the gossip sooner than most.

Tom Buckingham recalls former jockey Graham Thorner announcing his retirement midway through an afternoon's racing and he remembers too his typical superstition. 'Graham had a thing about green. He wouldn't ride with a green saddle pad. But one day at Newton Abbot after he'd fallen in the first and had five more rides I had nothing left but a green one to give him. He rode the winner of the next and from then on insisted on a green pad for every race.'

The recently retired Hywel Davies, he says, never went back to Doncaster after a horrific fall in which his horse cartwheeled on to him and Hywel actually 'died' for two minutes on the way to hospital. It was on that occasion, allegedly, that the irrepressible John Francome eased the weighing room tension by placing a pair of boots upside-down on the floor and calling out, 'Come on, Hywel, it's all right. You can come out now.'

The room is filling up. Leather-jacketed Adrian Maguire, leader by four in the jockeys' table, and with chief rival Richard Dunwoody sidelined by suspension for the forthcoming Cheltenham meeting, breezes in, body-language exuding confidence from every pore. Jamie Osborne, lying third, arrives in a natty green sports jacket, looking like a chorister on the day out from an expensive Cathedral school. But the first race is an undistinguished field of novice chasers and top jockeys like those two won't be risking injury on such uncertain conveyances the week before Cheltenham. When I comment on the number of smokers Andy Townsend, one of the Buckingham team of valets, says: 'Well, it's a novice chase, isn't it?' Enough said.

It's a contest for up-and-coming jockeys like Guy Upton and Chris Maude, for juniors in big stables like Robert Bellamy, as careful and elegant tying his neck stock as a bride's father at a wedding, and for riders like Ronnie Beggan.

Though fresh from a couple of winners in Scotland, Ronnie has never quite caught on with a fashionable stable and, like many riders outside the top twenty, has to take what he can get to pay the bills.

Ronnie Beggan is out of luck here, having to pull up. But as a man who's got his sideline secured, being just four hours' flying time short of a pilot's licence, he comes back looking happy enough.

Robert Bellamy's chance has gone when his horse blunders four out, though he plugs on for place money. The finish is fought out between Chris Maude, riding the 20/1 grey outsider Beach Bum, and Guy Upton on the favourite Los Caballeros, trained by his regular employer Simon Christian. Upton, who'd expected to win, gets a consoling pat from Maudie back in the changing room. It's one of the typical ironies of racing. Blonde permit-holder Judy Young, whose first winner it is, reveals that it is Guy Upton who has done all the hard work in schooling Beach Bum in her three-horse yard, only to end up frustrating the hopes of his main stable and losing a winner he'd counted on.

There's a shout from the Clerk of the Scales for amateur Gerry Hogan, who took a nasty-looking tumble from Hermes Harvest. Having parted company with his mount he doesn't have to weigh in. But after a fall he does have to go to the doctor to be passed fit to go on riding. 'If they stay in there too long saying "I'll be out in a minute" you know they're worse than they're pretending to be, trying not to get stood down,' says Derek Blake.

The bustle is on now as jockeys weigh out for the second race. All over the room are enough lean young men in ladies' nylon tights to send a transvestite club into a collective swoon. It gets cold out there in the saddle in paperweight nylon breeches. There's not much hair on the naked chests. If there was they'd probably shave it off to save weight . . .

As they wander about in various stages of undress with the occasional lady rider slipping in, fixedly eyes front, to collect her 'parcel' of colours from the valets, you do see why one young trainer's wife, formerly a leading lady rider herself, is in demand for her after-dinner speech entitled 'Jockey's Willies'.

Among the riders in this second race, a handicap hurdle, is John Kavanagh. During the first, he had limped down the passage and stretched out on a couch in the drying room. Physio 'Rabbit' Slattery, one of four employed by the Jockey Club to minister to the battered brigade of jockeys, has been easing his aches and pains after a broken leg. It is another racing dynasty. The Slatterys ride and train, and Rabbit's mother is Mary Bromiley, famous for her cures of both injured riders and their horses.

The hurdle is won smoothly by Yorkshire raider Brave Buccaneer, ridden by Northern jockey Peter Niven. It may be there, but there is no obvious sign of North/South rivalry as the other riders congratulate him on return. Watching the television re-run in the snack bar after the race, which shows how he had to keep his mount up to the job in the closing stages, 'Niv' displays no emotion. He sounded more excited earlier about having made it to Newbury from near Doncaster in two hours twenty minutes.

Cigarette behind his ear, Dean Gallagher, unlucky in his two rides today, says that he drives fifty to sixty thousand miles a year, even though he can frequently share the journeys with other Lambourn-based jockeys. Most reckon to trade in their cars every ten months or so. Never, never buy a second-hand car from a jockey. Behind the steering wheel they are all hard riders.

The next race, a handicap chase, goes to Jamie Osborne, riding Tipp Mariner from the out-of-form Simon Sherwood stable, backed down from 8/1 to 13/2. Jockeys, of course, are forbidden to bet. So, more surprisingly, are valets. But talking afterwards to racecourse staff I seem to have been the only one not in on the secret that the horse was well fancied.

The occasional jockey has been known, of course, to fancy a tickle. One Newbury weighing room story is of the top jockey who was unwise enough to bet openly in the ring one day. Spotting a steward out of the corner of his eye, and having no ride in the next race, he jumped into his car, drove the three miles home, changed all his clothes and reappeared in the weighing room, convincing the suspicious steward who had been looking for him that it had been a case of mistaken identity.

Moods are swinging up and down in the changing room today. After a good ride jockeys swagger a little, slap the table with their whips. After a poor run they sit gloomily through the TV replay with a consoling cigarette.

Mark Perrett, whose mount King's Curate jumped like a stag early on as the 11/8 favourite in the third race only to trail in a distant and lifeless fourth, looks disconsolate. That's a Cheltenham hope blown up. The ever-present Osborne grin though seems wider still.

Irish accents are in abundance about the changing room. And you can discern too two distinct physical types. Many of the Irishmen, like Adrian Maguire, Dean Gallagher and John Kavanagh seem shorter, more compact and muscular with some of the English jockeys taller, lean and spare, obviously having to work harder to do the ten stone. All though look like a human equivalent of the terrier section at Cruft's, strutting, wiry, perky heads tousled by the constant changes of headgear. You can't help noticing too the signs of the fearsome catalogue of injuries most of them suffer. There are the bumps and knobbles on the collar bones, the puckered scars of surgery on leg injuries, the raking lines down someone's back as if he'd been run over by a harrow.

So regularly do the heroes of Dick Francis's books get beaten up that I've always suspected a streak of masochism in the average jump jockey. One Newbury official tells me there used to be a medical specialist's skeleton in an office at Lingfield. The jockeys, who one day dressed it in silks and left it on the scales, used to wander in to finger it and say, 'I've broken this one, and this, and this . . .'

Fortunately there are no serious injuries in the fourth race, another handicap steeplechase won by Adrian Maguire on Di Haine's Spree Cross. But a spectacular tumble three out for the popular Simon McNeill, for whom Lucky Again proves anything but, draws a sympathetic groan from the jockeys watching. When he comes in Rabbit Slattery leads him straight to her treatment table. 'It's the next day they notice it,' she says.

Simon McNeill is in no hurry to see the doctor, fearing the dread red-ink entry on his jockey's passport which will mean he's stood down for two days. He has three rides at Stratford tomorrow, two of them fancied, and is irritated that an ambulance man has alarmed people by suggesting he'd taken a blow which had left him unable to speak. 'The only reason I couldn't speak was because I was bloody well winded.'

Simon says, 'When I was younger I used to bounce up immediately to convince others I was OK. Now I lie there until *I'm* sure I'm OK.'

He puts off the evil moment as long as he can but in the end he is stood down. Most of us wouldn't ride so much as a bicycle for three weeks after such a tumble. He can't wait to be throwing half a ton of horse at a fence again. Grinning ruefully he watches the replay, the horse seemingly part-rolling on him after a spectacular tip-up: 'Oooh, the dirty bastard. I'll have him . . .' But he doesn't mean it.

Adrian Maguire watches the replay intently, stealing a puff from John Kavanagh's cigarette. After 130 winners already this season does he need to? 'You're always on a high after a winner. You'll go back and look again to keep it going. But you learn too about your mistakes. Should you have popped one in before a fence? You can see better on TV too what the others were doing around you.'

Watching too as Jamie Osborne asks, 'How many winners has Woody had today?' is Mick Fitzgerald. One eye is almost completely closed, the other black and bruised. He's dabbing at a nose still bleeding from a resetting operation the day before after being kicked in the face at Fontwell. But he's happy as Larry, having learned today that he'll be riding the talented Remittance Man in the Champion Chase at Cheltenham next week, one of the rides lost by Dunwoody through his suspension.

Newbury's fifth race today is a hunter chase with just four runners, which turns into something of a procession behind Andros Prince, ridden by Mike Felton. What the punters didn't see was the fetching red tights underneath the breeches, the snazziest in the jockeys' room today. 'He guessed the third last but he jumped well all the way,' Felton tells Adrian Maguire, who's ready like many of the professionals with a word of encouragement and advice.

Suddenly though comes a flurry. Blond, elegant young claimer Guy Lewis, who's been sitting there nursing his mobile phone, dashes into the weighing room half-dressed, chivied by the valets. Graham Bradley, driving up from Lingfield for a fancied ride in

the last, a novices' handicap hurdle, clearly isn't going to make it
the requisite fifteen minutes before the race to clear his passport
and report in, so Lewis has the spare ride for trainer Paul Nicholls
on Bond Jnr.

Two minutes after deadline in bursts the irrepressible Brad. He's
been eighty minutes on the road, stuck for the last twenty behind
a tractor. To get to the course he's run the last mile and a half,
begged a lift from an old lady and scraped his knee and elbow after
hurdling the central reservation barrier on the road without a horse.
'All that and I've missed a winner too,' he mutters, feeling his
bruises.

On the strength of that comment I nip out and double my bet
on Bond Jnr, coming back to find Brad explaining himself to the
'Stipe', the stipendiary steward, who lets him off without a fine
because he is considered to have allowed enough time to get to the
course and has been unlucky. He could have had fine added to
injury and lost riding fee. But not this time. 'Thank you, sir, I
appreciate it.' Two minutes later he's settled in front of the TV in
a towel asking Rabbit for a plaster for his grazes.

Guy Lewis has a decent run on Bond Jnr but three out he weakens
and it's another Maguire winner as Nick Gaselee's Glentower
comes home by seven lengths from Jamie Osborne on Castle Court.
It's the irony of racing again. Maguire rides rarely for Gaselee and
the man who was brought in to 'switch on' the greenish Glentower
over three hurdles on the gallops early this morning was his keen
rival Richard Dunwoody, riding today at Lingfield. John Kavanagh
calls out, 'You owe me a drink, Adrian. That was my saddle and
my girths.' But the man who got the drink later was Dunwoody,
who found it already waiting for him when he walked into the
Queens in East Garston, courtesy of Adrian Maguire.

The changing room empties rapidly as lifts are shared out for
the morning. There's no time for larks on a businesslike day like
this. There's no famous victory to celebrate and all eyes are looking
forward to Cheltenham. For all the famous tales of Champagne
Charlie jockeys today's breed look more natural with a mobile
phone in their hands than with a glass. The number cloths have
been packed away, the last nibbles of lean meat and celery have
gone from the snack bar. Soon the only people left are Tom
Buckingham, Pat Taylor and their teams, scrubbing girth straps,

checking the labels on breeches and bundling up the gear for tomorrow. Another racing day in the jockeys' room closes as it began: to the hum of the washing machine and the roar of the tumble dryer.

Day In, Day Out

GEOFF O'HARA

Give a little, take a little, depending upon the accuracy of your dickory dock, it is around midday when I forsake the carbon-laden air of Hacker Street and enter the alcoholic haze of the Hanging Tassel.

And it gives me no small surprise to espy Abe Zimmerman, turf accountant and betting shop proprietor, gazing disconsolately into the bottom of an empty glass. However, it's not the emptiness of the glass which occasions my amazement, 'cos when it comes to the vanishing trick with booze, Abe is nothing if not an artist and a past master.

No, what surprises me is the fact that Abe should be absent from his Hacker Street empire at midday. Because any reader of the *Sporting Life*, and most bookmakers are, will be aware that the first race at Hambry Park is due for despatch at 12.15. But I have been brought up in the 'mind your own bloody business' tradition, so I do not remark upon the fact that my bookmaker is absent from his post when he should be busily attending to the requirements of the punting public – and the Customs and Excise brigade.

In any event, I would be reluctant to mention such a distressing subject as Customs and Excise to Abe as it is a known and lamented fact that dear old Abe has never been the same man since Chancellors stuck their sticky fingers into the bookmaking tills of Britain. So I tell Mischa the Minder to refill Abe's glass and I'll take a little of the same myself. Whereupon Abe proceeds to unfold the following tear-jerking tale.

'Y'know, Brogan,' says Abe, 'the bookmaking game is definitely not what it was. Take yesterday and I wish to blazes somebody had taken it. It is coming up for the half past two race and a right layabout strolls into my shop. I can see straight off that he is definitely in the bony and flint division. In fact, judging from the state of his threads, I will be very fortunate indeed if he does not relieve me of a gross of give-away pens, make full use of the office carsey and blow without having a punt.

'Anyway,' continues Abe, 'the geezer comes up to the counter and has himself a pound on the fav in the 2.30. Of course, the fav goes by at evens and the geezer is a pound to the good and my settler pays him in fifty pence pieces. Just to annoy him, I suppose.

'Well, this finger strolls out to take the air, which is the only commodity the Government have not put the tin tacks on and the next thing I know he is back putting a fiver's worth of fifty pences on Stamping Cat. Stamping Cat goes in at 11/2 and this layabout is twenty-seven and a half quid in front. And all I coulda copped for in the first place is a pound. And in the second place he got his fiver's worth of fifty pences out of one of my fruit machines, which I have strategically placed in the back room at Charlie's chip shop.'

Having heard this sad saga thus far I am indeed distressed. Not only am I distressed on Abe's account, but also on account of myself. I fancied Stamping Cat myself, and neglected to follow up my fancy because I was actively engaged in trying to extract the Jackpot from one of Abe's machines just at the time when Stamping Cat was cantering in at the races.

So I give Abe a generous measure of 'tut-tuts' and 'Oh! dear me's' and also a 'Well, I never' as a bonus and Abe continues as follows: 'When the geezer has relieved me of the twenty-seven and a half sovs he promptly leaves my establishment, goes into a spieler in Caftan Court and gets himself nicely elephant's trunk on the type of cheap hooch being peddled in such low-life joints as are springing up in the manor nowadays.

'Having got himself well and truly steamed up in the spieler, he returns to my punting parlour and comes up to the counter for a tenner on the 4.30 fav. By the time he asks for the bet, the race is nearly over and the fav is well out in front. So, naturally my manager says, "No bet." The fav goes by and you can imagine the state of the punter.

'He is annoyed, incensed and highly aggravated. So much so that he heaves an empty Scotch bottle, which he is carrying just for the sake of old times, right through my plate glass window. Before you can say all in run or not, six kinds of hell are let loose.

'The bogies are all over the gaff, trying to sort out the bother, the irate punter fetches one of my clerks a fourpenny one in the kisser and in the excitement my manager forgets to have a fifty on trap two in the last at Winterbottom Heath, which is running up from an accumulator. It obliges at 7/2. So, one way and another it was a day I coulda done without.'

I am well on the way to thinking this is the saddest thing since small boys were sent up chimneys when Abe goes on again.

'When I get to the office this morning, I find that my plate glass windows are not insured, my manager wants to leave the betting business and become a probation officer, Inspector Lubbock has been on the blower to suggest I run my office in a more orderly manner, and two strongarm boys from Islington Johnny's mob are waiting to see if I wish to pay protection and live longer! Me, with my worries, I should wish to live longer?'

So Abe goes on his way to Sadie Lejeune's place and his parting shot was, 'It's not better than evens she blows me out on account of I'm jinxed.' So I drink my drink and make for Ponsonby Court. Well, how can I go and have a punt at Abe's place? It wouldn't feel right to touch him up for a few quid having heard his tale of woe.

As I drive back to Myrtle's flat, I am pleasurably anticipating the reception I will get from my everloving. She will certainly think her ship has come in when she realizes that Brogan is back by hearth and home before the last race has been run. But you never know with women. They're as unpredictable as racehorses, even though they're better to look at. Leastways, that's the way it is with Myrtle.

As soon as I grace the lounge of 26 Ponsonby Court, she sounds off about I wouldn't be home so early if I hadn't done my pieces punting at Abe's place.

Well no man likes to be put in the wrong, especially when he's really in the right, so Myrtle and I have a real exchange of highly expletive adjectives and the upshot of it all is that I cop for my Crombie and hightail it back to Hacker Street as fast as the Jag will go.

It's too late for the punting caper so I sneak into the Hanging Tassel via the back door, 'cos I know that Mischa the Minder will be willing to set 'em up and lend a sympathetic ear. And who do I espy gazing disconsolately into the bottom of an empty glass? You've guessed it, Abe Zimmerman. Yes, Sadie Lejeune has given him his marching orders on account of she was expecting her sister to tea, or some such nonsense.

So Abe and I go into the commiseration caper and by the time Mischa the Minder heaves us out into Hacker Street we are very much the worse for wear and Abe is nothing less than downright obstreperous. In fact, he is so obstreperous that he picks up an empty milk bottle and lobs it clean through the newly repaired plate glass window of his own betting shop.

And that is how we come to be sharing a flowery dell in the Gendarmerie waiting to be charged on the drunk and disorderly lark. Abe can make his own arrangements from here on in, but Myrtle, for pity's sake, bail me out, 'cos you I really love.

Now the latest bit of bother I'm in is all down to Abe Zimmerman's bird Sadie Lejeune, my bird Myrtle, and Abe's wife Rachel. But mind you, if I'm in trouble I must say I'm in very good company. Old Abe is in it with me. In right up to his fat neck.

It's thisaway. Having spent a cold and comfortless night in the cells we come up before the judiciary looking like a couple of third-rate comedians who have just had the razz at a fourth-rate music hall. And though we may look like a brace of buffoons it is fairly obvious from the remarks of the penance pedlar that he does not find us at all amusing. In fact, he fines us twenty-five sovs apiece and sends us on our way anything but rejoicing.

Which explains how we come to be pounding the pitiless pavements of Hacker Street at an hour when most of the citizens are munching their last round of toast and turning the pages of the *Sporting Life* with buttery fingers.

What is more, the weather in the area of Hacker Street is anything but inviting. In fact there is a cold, biting wind blowing along the street, designed to send the brass monkeys away in droves. And though I am encased in my Crombie and Abe is well wrapped in his Vicuna, we are both of the opinion that this is indeed a cold hard world.

I know only too well that the time is not ripe for me to return to Myrtle; she'd give me a right going over with no punches pulled;

and Abe is well aware that there is no welcome awaiting him, either at his home or at Sadie's place. So it would seem that we are two orphans of the storm with every hand against us.

However, acting upon the old saying 'Any port in a storm,' we shuffle disconsolately into the Hanging Tassel. And it is within the precincts of this haven of hangabouts that everything starts to happen. For who is propping up the bar, in the company of as nice a bit of homework as ever I've seen, but little Harry Kaye.

Introductions are exchanged and the bird turns out to be a cousin of Harry's several times removed, Cynthia Surcingle.

Like I said, this Cynthia is a bit of all right. In fact she is a bird I would not mind flying the coop for at any time, especially now, as I do not stand too well with Myrtle.

But it is obvious that Abe is way ahead of me in this line of thought and before we have consumed more than three large brandies to keep the cold out, he has convinced one and all that a day at the races would be a very good idea indeed.

So we arrange to meet again at the Tassel prior to going on to Sandown, and Abe and me nip across the street to Tony's tonsorial establishment for a shave and a shoeshine. (Well, you've got to look the part if Cynthia Surcingle is among the starters.) And when Tony turns us out I must say we would do credit to the front page of a male fashion magazine.

Abe is groomed to perfection and is poncing about like a penguin on a pogo stick.

Me, I look like an out-of-work film director on his way to the East Finchley Film Festival, and though we are Sandown-bound, it is obvious that the affections of Cynthia Surcingle are of more importance to us than the possibility of picking winners from a very trappy card.

In fact Abe is far from subtle and even suggests that I should stay in town and keep an eye on his office for him. So I tell him cobblers to that and if his office needs so much supervision, he should stay in town himself.

So off we go to Sandown; Little Harry and me up front and Abe and the bird very closely closeted in the back of the Jag. Yes, he's drawn very well is old Abe, but I figure that I'll be there at the post when it comes to a tight finish, I'll be weighed in with Cynthia and Abe will be doing nothing but raising objections.

Leastways, that's how I see it until we get on to the course and Cynthia excuses herself to go across to the weighing room.

Naturally, the fact that Cynthia Surcingle has business in the vicinity of the weighing room is most intriguing to me and I ask Harry Kaye, 'What's it all about?'

'Oh,' replies Harry, 'Cynthia is engaged to that very good amateur rider Freddy Frogmore, and doubtless she has gone to wish him much mozzle on account of him riding Lonesome Lady in the gentleman's event this afternoon.' Well, this is all news to me and very distressing too; here I am at Sandown with the sole intention of impressing Cynthia, only to discover that she is engaged to a jockey and an amateur at that.

Abe does not take too kindly to the news, either. He has only two interests in life, birds and his betting business. And as he sees it, if the bird is beyond his reach, well, he should be back in his betting office scrutinizing his security systems or whatever bookmakers do during the day's racing.

So it's a case of two disappointed Lotharios finding themselves at Sandown feeling a degree or two under on account of having a night in the cells and having consumed a few bevies and no breakfast.

But we are out in the air and the runners are on their way to the post, the layers are shouting the odds and all around are highly animated indeed. In fact, it's a part of the British scene that I am proud to be associated with, always assuming I do not do my pieces in the process.

The books ask for odds over the first fav and Abe and I give it a miss. Little Harry has a monkey to get him four centuries and the lovely Cynthia has a few bob placed on the outsider of the party.

The fav goes in by a distance, the outsider scrambles into third place and Harry and Cynthia are having a ball.

Me and Abe? Well, we're just having a day out. On Harry's say-so we have a crack at one in the next but it comes a purler at the open ditch and I'm beginning to wish I'd taken Abe's offer to keep sights on his punting parlour.

So the next race on the card is the gentleman's event and as

Cynthia Surcingle has connections among the cavaliers we have to take her advice and get on Lonesome Lady.

I must say here and now that when it comes to riding, this Freddy Frogmore is no slouch, and if he handles the fair Cynthia with as much determination as he bestows upon Lonesome Lady, they should have a very fortunate future indeed.

We go in as soon as the betting opens up and after putting Freddy Frogmore on a 6/1 to fifty quid, we are happy indeed to fill our boots at all offers down to 7/2. So that when we mount the stands to view the contest, we are as anxious about the outcome as is Cynthia Surcingle.

And Freddy Frogmore gives us no cause for alarm. Quietly confident is the only way to describe his handling of the mare. In fact, he goes by the post with several lengths to spare and even manages to smile for the television cameras as he canters in.

As you can imagine, our enthusiasm knows no bounds.

We rush from the stands and make for the winner's enclosure and as soon as Freddy weighs in we surround him and accord him a reception fit for a hero, which he undoubtedly is. Cynthia kisses Freddy, Freddy shakes hands all round, Abe kisses Cynthia, I kiss Cynthia and there is much joyful embracing. In fact, in the confusion, Little Harry kisses Abe but that is only down to enthusiasm, so don't go getting any wrong ideas.

It's pretty obvious that Abe and I are well outpaced when it comes to who is taking Cynthia home from Sandown. But we've had a very nice tickle and no one can begrudge Freddy Frogmore his fair lady.

So Abe and me bid a fond farewell to all and sundry and set off for London. And as Abe opines over a steak and a bottle of Nuits St Georges, 'Y'know, Brogan, Cynthia is one woman it's been a pleasure to know.' 'Agreed, Abe,' says I, and we spend a fair portion of our winnings and some of the evening in drinking the health of birds, racehorses and amateur riders.

As you can imagine, we are in a very fulsome state when we roll into the Hanging Tassel about a quarter to ten. And straight off I can see that things are not as they should be. For there, sitting on a high stool and looking very hoity-toity indeed, is my Myrtle.

'Well, Brogan,' she opens up, 'and where have you been all day?' I'm straight in with the alibi. 'I've been helping Abe out in the betting office, darling.'

'Well,' replies Myrtle, 'if that is so, perhaps you'll be good enough to explain how I am seeing you on my TV screen this afternoon. At Sandown with a bird and going through a right little love scene in the unsaddling enclosure.'

So there it is. I'm in lumber again and by the time I've pacified Myrtle there will be little change left out of my Sandown winnings.

But it's no better for Abe, 'cos Mischa the Minder tells him that both his wife Rachel and his popsy Sadie have been on the blower for him. And when Abe backs out of the phone booth he is very white about the gills indeed.

'Why in hell's name didn't someone tell me Sandown was on TV?' says he. 'This little lot will cost me a bomb to straighten out. Sadie is doing her nut about me being with a bird at the races and my wife, Rachel, is demanding I should buy her a bigger television so she can see how I would look in the part of the ageing Romeo!'

So that's how it is with Abe and me. We were just born under the wrong stars.

Myrtle has returned to Ponsonby Court in a taxi, also in high dudgeon. Abe has slunk off to lick his wounds in the back room at his betting office.

As for me, I'm favourite for a night in a steam bath. But I wonder what Freddy Frogmore is doing to keep his weight down.

Well, I suppose things could be worse. I'll stand Myrtle a little black dress out of the winnings and maybe she'll go easy on the black looks. 'Cos you, Myrtle, I love.

Cartmel

JOHN BUDDEN

Cartmel is the smallest, most inaccessible yet hugely popular and profitable racecourse in Britain. It is not unknown for upwards of twenty thousand racegoers – and the term is used loosely – to squeeze themselves through hedgerow, ancient turnstile or five-bar gate to attend the two-day August Bank Holiday meeting.

The executive take all Sunday morning to add up the takings and the irony of it all is that the racecourse commentator is the only spectator who is in a position to catch more than a passing glimpse of the action.

He, too, is left to make up his own lines as the leaders sweep left-handed at the end of the back straight to disappear for approximately half a mile behind the impenetrable combination of fairground big-wheel and 'Scout hut' copse.

Not so long ago Cartmel races were on a par with a local point-to-point. Today they have taken on cult status and the villagers' determination to prevent any expansion of the fixture list is readily understandable.

Cartmel lies near the foot of the Cark peninsula within spitting distance of the northern extremity of Morecambe Bay, surrounded by the rugged beauty of the Cumbrian fells and cut off from the inquisitive gaze of the M6 trailblazers by a mass of twisting, narrow, sunken lanes that require a detailed large-scale road map and a magnifying glass to trace with any accuracy.

As most inhabitants of the Home Counties or the inner city regard Cumbria as a remote region at least two days' march from civilization, the arrival of such enthusiastic camp followers matches the miracle of the feeding of the five thousand.

On reflection the multitudes are more concerned with the beer glass than the stomach and some never even leave the pub-encircled village square until the winner of the final novice hurdle has long been scrubbed down and returned to the cocoon of his waiting horsebox.

For 360 days in the year Cartmel is the sleepy preserve of its residents, an interesting mixture of retired gentlefolk, farming yeoman stock and the yuppy interloper from the service industry, keen to escape from the urban sprawl of nearby Barrow-in-Furness.

Hugh Cavendish of Holker Hall is the benevolent despot of the parish. He owns the land on which the racecourse stands plus a great deal of the property and farmland within a ten-mile radius of his stately home, which is pronounced 'Hooker', boasts the finest rose garden in the North-West and is one of the very few ancestral piles still in private ownership.

Happily for racing enthusiasts Hugh Cavendish is keen on the sport. He has a couple of jumpers in training with Gordon Richards at Greystoke and whenever his duties in the House of Lords allow, he is as familiar a sight at Cartmel as Labour's Robin Cook is at Kelso.

It is impossible to overlook the Cavendish influence in Cartmel. The largest and most comfortable hotel-cum-public-house in the village bears the family's coat of arms. The Lord of the Manor retains the right to appoint the local vicar to his living and every worthwhile institute or organization will list the name of Cavendish as either its patron or trustee.

By and large the inhabitants are content with the status quo. Cartmel is a prosperous, secure community, content to enjoy the economic bonus of a thriving tourist trade in the holiday season, yet equally happy to retreat into its comfortable shell for eight months of the year, sample the goods of the well-stocked grocer, enjoy the unsurpassed beauty of the surrounding countryside and drink at their leisure in their own local.

Such simple privileges are torn from their grasp during the five days that Cartmel plays host to the racing circus. Many no doubt pay a timely visit to the well-set priory, below whose towering walls huddle the hotchpotch of whitewashed cottages, substantial villas and heavily beamed farmhouses that make up the village.

Their prayers will be short and simple. They ask for rain – persistent and heavy enough to discourage the beer-swilling hordes in the village square and bring about an abortive end to the noisy clamour of the funfair, which long-standing local statutes have granted permission to be held on the common land that forms the lower half of the racecourse.

God, it seems, takes a dim view of the residents' NIMBY attitude towards other people's enjoyment. More often than not the sun shines at Cartmel and acres of bare flesh add to the locals' discomfiture.

Their hands are tied. Historically racing is welcome on the Cartmel green over the period of both the Spring and Autumn Bank Holidays. The Racecourse Company have the law on their side. They also have the support of the tradesfolk, whose receipts rocket through the roof when the sun shines. So much so that the application to stage a fifth day's racing on the Wednesday before the May holiday weekend was approved without demur in the late eighties.

They have raced at Cartmel since the middle of the seventeenth century. Sources claim that the monks of the nearby priory entertained themselves in their leisure time by organizing competitive racing on mules: no course bookmakers naturally, but little doubt that some form of illegal betting helped to enliven the occasion.

The first written evidence of racing at Cartmel relates to the meeting of 1856, held on the present site adjacent to the village and now used by both the local cricket and soccer clubs on all but five days in the year.

Early meetings were on the flat but by the end of the century Cartmel Races had switched codes. Probably because the local farmers were keen hunting men, the annual meeting on the Whit Monday became a National Hunt fixture. Jump racing has continued without interruption, except for the war years, until the present day. In 1947 the Whit Saturday was added to the Spring holiday meeting and in the early sixties the August dates were added to the calendar. The extra Wednesday fixture is a recent addition.

Between the wars the Whit Monday fixture was saved from extinction by the combined efforts of local landowners and the Pain family.

There is still a race run in memory of Horace D. Pain and his son Colonel Davy Pain remains the Course Chairman, dispensing champagne by the magnum to every winning owner. Father and son, solicitors by profession, devoted no small measure of their out of office hours to the welfare of Cartmel. They were assisted by men of the calibre of George Dickinson, father of the late Tony Dickinson, the famous National Hunt trainer whose son Michael created history by saddling the first five horses home in the 1983 Cheltenham Gold Cup. Dickinson senior owned an all-grass farm at Cark-in-Cartmel and was a director of the racecourse for over fifty years. 'He saved it from flapping,' recalled Tony with some pride.

Until the sixties Cartmel was the preserve of the sporting amateur. Professional jockeys were in the minority. There was an unmistakable atmosphere of Gentlemen versus Players. Picnic hampers, Chablis and champagne littered the members' enclosure and prize money might conceivably have covered the cost of a full tank of petrol.

Davy Pain sowed the seeds of change on 1962. The Colonel introduced sponsorship to Cartmel, obtaining backers for six of the twelve races, the first time that a small National Hunt course had gone commercial. Sixteen years later Pain played his trump card. He appointed Major Tim Riley as Clerk of the Course, a decision that was to convert Cartmel from a holiday gaff into the most charismatic and admired racecourse in Britain.

As General Manager and more recently Managing Director, Tim Riley operated without any permanent staff. His motto remains 'We are professional amateurs rather than amateur professionals.'

It was a nice distinction but an eminently sound one. The Major's assistant secretary was a retired telephone manager; his course foreman a shift foreman at Glaxo's in Ulverston; the stable manager a coal merchant.

Value for money and the necessity for racing to be fun were Tim Riley's twin aims. He also realized that with the opening of the M6 and the high holiday profile of the Lake District as a National Park, there was an ever-growing source of customers to be tapped.

By resourceful use of the media and by provision of user-friendly facilities, Tim Riley created an on-course jamboree built around the day's racing but at the same time satisfying the needs of the complete family. He expanded the funfair, introduced trade stalls for the ladies, encouraged the local landlords to offer generous discounts and used the increase in profits to improve the condition of the racecourse and increase the volume of prize money.

Tim suffered a serious brain haemorrhage in the summer of 1993 and, though making an astonishing recovery, has by necessity been forced to relinquish his duties.

His successor, Charles Barnett of Aintree fame, will only need to tinker with the fine tuning to maintain the bonanza. Racing at Cartmel is a unique experience. Go once and you are hooked for life.

To appreciate the full flavour of the occasion, a few ground rules require attention.

The journey to the course is itself a strategic exercise. Whether travelling from north, south or east (those coming from the west must be locals and therefore will be familiar with the lay of the land) the route must lie along the A590 from exit number 36 on the M6 in the direction of Barrow-in-Furness.

Engage automatic pilot until passing the only Little Chef en route. At the next roundabout sheeplike racegoers follow the AA signs 'to the races' and find themselves enmeshed in the tailback of a three-mile traffic jam.

Shrewder parties continue directly to Grange-over-Sands. Drive straight through this still-Victorian holiday resort and once clear of the main shopping centre keep a careful eye skinned for the signpost to Cartmel.

Once detected it is only a matter of two miles to the village. Progress will be at walking pace on the approach to the market square but aim steadfastly for the Paddock entrance and do not apply the brakes until safely housed in the members' enclosure. The ticket may cost £12 but is worth every penny.

A false move to the public car park is tantamount to a one-way ticket to Hades: abandoned amidst a noxious cloud of beefburger and onions, surrounded by the sweaty nightcap brigade and deafened by the proximity of the noisiest funfair north of Blackpool Tower. The cardinal rule about racing at Cartmel is the necessity to follow the road signs 'to the Paddock'.

The racecourse, you must understand, is a perfect oval split diagonally through the middle by the finishing straight. To the north of this great divide lies the peaceful haven of the Paddock enclosure, the Chairman's champagne tent, the only usable lavatories and the Tote.

To the south lie the 'off-course' entertainments – loud, crowded, teeming with hot, sweaty lager louts and a fair smattering of pickpockets – the police patrol in pairs and your car aerial will be lucky to survive the hour.

Rule number two concerns the picnic. On arrival immediately unfurl the rug and unpack the plates, glasses and bottles of wine. Note the use of the plural, as the canny racegoer will have arrived with at least an hour to spare before the first race and a single bottle is not going to last the distance. More important is the need to establish territory. Every inch of the car park will eventually be covered but Cartmel members are quintessentially well-mannered and the thought of mowing down the cold chicken and Chablis will automatically stop them in their tracks.

The ideal parking position at Cartmel is in the far corner beyond the actual Paddock with the front bumper wedged against the running rail. To achieve this pole position will require arrival well before midday but the effort, if successful, will pay a mammoth dividend. From this vantage spot watchers can command an uncluttered view of the runners lining up to start and the first mile of the action. You will be the envy of the enclosure and will need the patience of Job to hold your advantage throughout the afternoon.

Cartmel was once a paradise for dogs. That was in pre-Riley times. Nowadays, dog ownership is a trap. My Labrador bitch sought every avenue to find her way to the woods opposite the course but her progress was blocked at every turn.

Eventually she was humiliated into squatting amidst parked cars and picnics – it was a messy business to remove and the litter bins were conspicuous by their absence! Far better to leave the hound at home, complete with access to the sofa and the Pedigree Chum supply.

To back a winner at Cartmel is the equivalent of selecting the first four home in the Grand National in their correct order.

In a field of six, and the average turn-out for each race will be about this number, the soundest advice is cross out the two favourites and cover the remaining four runners – this way one is morally bound to unearth a long-priced winner.

Horses previously successful round the course should be treated like gold dust and lady riders with nut-cracking thighs must never be allowed to start unbacked.

Stories of skulduggery at Cartmel are legion but easily the most outstanding occasion of this type took place in the summer of 1974.

The Gay Future affair had all the ingredients of a perfectly planned and brilliantly executed coup. Its ultimate failure was triggered off by human error of the most basic type.

The successful outcome of the plot required the collusion of the trainer, the jockey, the off-course backers and unwittingly the bookmakers on the course itself.

Irish-based trainer Edward O'Grady was to prepare the real Gay Future on the gallops. A lesser horse with the same name was shipped across the water to join the stable of Tony Collins at Troon, ostensibly to be got ready for an early autumn campaign. Tony had been a permit holder for some ten seasons. Results proved that he knew the time of day and it would be nothing out of the ordinary for his horses to be running early in the season, particularly at Cartmel, where his colours were familiar.

By profession Tony Collins was and still is a successful stockbroker. He had a reputation for doing battle with the ring and was only too happy to be associated with the plan. His part in the strategy should have been simple. He was to declare four of his horses for Bank Holiday Monday. Ankerwyke, if recollection is correct, was entered for Southwell. Opera Cloak was due to visit Plumpton and both Racionzer and Gay Future were declared for Cartmel.

The latter, appearing in the Collins's colours for the first time, purported to be the stables' second choice. Both horses were entered for the Ulverston Novices' Hurdle but whereas Racionzer was to be professionally ridden, Gay Future's intended jockey was the little-known amateur Mr J. (for Jimmy) McNeill.

Tony Collins sent an empty box down the A74 and the M6 to meet up with the transport containing the real Gay Future, now safely landed from Ireland.

The two horses were swopped and the Edward O'Grady-prepared Gay Future wended his merry way to Cartmel.

Meanwhile owner Tony Murphy, a Cork millionaire, had organized a posse of Irish brickies in London to swamp the betting shops with small-denominational doubles and trebles covering all three of the Collins-trained horses. The multiple bets would of course all become singles if as previously planned the stable's runners at Plumpton and Southwell were withdrawn before coming under orders.

Tony Collins made one mistake. For a committed punter it was rather more than an error and even with hindsight it should have been avoided.

The two horses entered for the southern meetings failed to leave his stable at Troon. They were grazing happily in their respective paddocks.

Had the animals involved begun their journey south and, shall we say, failed to arrive because of a mechanical breakdown, no blame could possibly be laid at the trainer's door. The horses had left his yard en route to Southwell and Plumpton but their transport had lurched to a halt somewhere on the motorway network and they had been stranded – all above-board.

This precaution was not taken. Meanwhile Gay Future had arrived at Cartmel under the care of Eddie O'Grady's experienced stable lad 'Micky' Finn. He had been stabled at the racecourse the previous night and was galloped on the track shortly after dawn on the Monday to ensure that he was spot on for the afternoon's contest.

Down in London, Tony Murphy's Daimler was whisking his commission agents around the City. The runners were investing wagers of five, ten and fifteen pounds on doubles and trebles covering all three of the Collins horses. All went well until around midday an astute betting office manager smelled a rat. The bookies' early warning system was alerted and the edict went out – no more bets to be taken on the Collins trio. The layers' network had foiled a massive coup, but even so some £5000 had been wagered.

In normal circumstances it would have been easy for the major bookmakers to cut their losses to a minimum by backing Gay Future with office money and reducing its starting price to a miserly level.

Tony Murphy had been prepared for this contingency. Cartmel, he knew, had no blower links with either London or Glasgow. If Ladbrokes were to place money at the course, their representatives would have to make the trip personally and bring the cash with them.

The manager of their branch in Barrow was contacted with instructions to reach the course in time for the 4.20 and pile the money on Gay Future. He immediately hired a taxi but the lanes around Cartmel were jam-packed with holidaymakers and by the time the wretched fellow dashed breathless through the turnstiles the race had already been run.

The success of the coup depended to a large extent on Gay Future winning the race at long odds. The news that the gelding was now to be partnered by the experienced Irish amateur Tim Jones instead of the novice rider Jimmy McNeill could have attracted outside interest, so to offset any possible support for the horse, 'Micky' Finn rubbed soap suds into his flanks and upper legs to produce an effect akin to serious sweating as Gay Future paraded before the race. His compatriots moved anonymously among the bookmakers backing all the other runners. Their efforts were rewarded. Gay Future started at 10/1 and romped home by fifteen lengths from Canobie Key. The bookies squealed. Their security organization BOLA announced that payment of winning bets would be stopped prior to an official enquiry and investigations were immediately begun.

It was not long before detectives discovered that neither Ankerwyke nor Opera Cloak had ever left Troon. This, together with the revelation that the Gay Future who had won the Ulverston Novices, Hurdle was not in fact the horse of the same name who had been lodged with Tony Collins at Troon for the relevant period of qualification, was enough for the jury at Preston Crown Court to bring in a 'guilty' verdict. Murphy and Tony Collins were each fined £1000 and warned off the Turf.

As for Gay Future, he won again at Hexham, was then sold to John Banks, the ebullient bookmaker, and shortly afterwards died of a broken neck at Wetherby – a tragic end to a brilliant coup that could only have occurred at Cartmel.

Other little amusements at the Lakeland course pale into insignificance by comparison, though the story of the senior jockey's victory in the three-horse long distance chase still raises a titter.

The Cartmel circuit is an oval, little more than a mile in circumference. To the onlooker the number of laps that the horses have to take can be a matter of confusion. A rider, unaccustomed to the layout, is inclined to lose count.

During the seventies an experienced Cartmel pilot, now a much respected official, was partnering a dodgy stayer. He was lying second, a length adrift of the leader, as the field emerged from the wooded glade at the bottom end of the course.

Realizing that his mount was tying up beneath him, the senior jockey was about to accept defeat when the leader's rider, an ingenuous youngster having his first ride round Cartmel, turned and called across, 'We've still got one more circuit to go, haven't we, boss?' The veteran gave him the thumbs up, took a pull, and once his raw rival had passed the gap into the home straight, nipped round the bend to win unchallenged.

From that moment to this a couple of racecourse officials are positioned at the junction with a white painted rope to ensure that the riders always take the right course!

The appeal of Cartmel lies in its unique atmosphere, the beauty of its location and the proximity of its action.

The start is situated immediately outside the kitchen window of No 1, The Market Square. The owner herself could easily dispatch the runners with a wave of her drying-up cloth. The horses gallop so close to the parked cars that even the slowest and most bow-legged of three-mile chasers appears to be travelling faster than Nijinsky. The smell of bacon sizzling on the portable barbecues, mingling with the aroma of coffee, horse manure and fumes from the dodgem cars, is pure Cartmel.

Try it at least once; but unless you are the commentator, go for the experience and not for the racing.

How I Loved You

JAMES MORTON

As a child I was brought up by two maiden aunts in the Cotswolds. My scholastic education was topped up by my Uncle Roger, who had a grand passion for the Turf. He lived in a village some miles away. In truth he couldn't bear my aunts' dog, a mangy animal who was constantly sick, usually in the flowerbeds but all too often over his shoes; and so at the age of forty-five he left the family home and bought himself a cottage.

Telling my aunts we were going on a long and healthy walk, because I was supposed to be delicate, he would collect me in his battered Morris Eight and would take me on his regular outings to racehorse training establishments arranged under the pretext that he was thinking of having a leg in training. Roger looked up these forgotten and slightly suspect trainers in his old copy of the *Directory of the Turf* and made enquiries. He found it passed many a pleasant Sunday morning examining broken-down hurdlers whom the trainer was unsurprisingly keen to sell.

The conversation was always the same as rugs were taken off the backs of the animals, legs were felt, opinions of stable, preferably head, lads sought. 'Win one for you easily, sir; just had a bit of leg trouble, and he's back in hard work now.'

I wondered, after an inspection of the yard and champagne was served in the trainer's study under paintings – probably brought in – of winners of the Lincoln when it was run at the Carfax, just who was kidding whom. Once I found an equine *Rake's Progress* in photographs. On the trainer's desk there it was, a very flashy, self-satisfied-looking chesnut. 'Newbury, two-year-old Hungerford Maiden Stakes Div 1'. On the window sill: 'Wolverhampton, two-year-old stakes'; on another sill: 'Edinburgh, two-year-old selling stakes'. In the hall, 'Newbury, three-year-old novice hurdle'. 'Huntingdon, four-year-old novice hurdle'. 'Sedgefield, novice steeple-chase'. 'Devon and Exeter, novice selling steeplechase (claiming riders)'. I was wondering why the trainer kept this record of abject failure. 'Sold him abroad,' I heard a voice over my shoulder. 'Doing very well in Bahrain. Won the Emir's plate last month.'

The meetings always broke up with thanks, news that the horse was entered within the week at Wincanton and could run in Roger's own colours. 'Bound to get a place, although I really quietly fancy it meself to go all the way.' And promises from Roger to ring within twenty-four hours. Afterwards Roger would ask, as if the decision for the enterprise rested on my shoulders, 'Well, what do you think?' 'I'm not sure you could keep it from Lizzie,' he would continue, answering his own question. Lizzie was the elder sister. 'Not if it won.' 'You think she'll be cross even if it did?' asked Roger, adding before I could reply, 'Maybe you're right.'

I would take a close interest in the results for the next week or so to see if Roger's proposed purchase had won. I was invariably rewarded by seeing a note in the *Sporting Life*: Tailed Off or, even better, Pulled Up. Once, after we went back for a second inspection, I did actually think Roger would buy a leg, but when it came to it he never did. This time I did not have such satisfaction. The horse won twice in successive races. Roger never mentioned it.

What the Sunday mornings did do was to make me convinced that what I wanted was a horse of my own. When I was twenty-three Roger died and left me some money in his will. Along with the cheque from the solicitor was an envelope which was marked for my eyes only. In it Roger had written a note requesting that I should buy a horse with it, remarking that the money should buy a halfway decent animal and keep it in training for three years. Apparently he had not put the suggestion in the will itself for fear of bringing down Lizzie's wrath on him posthumously. He was always frightened of her. He need not have worried. She and his other sister had both pre-deceased him. Unfortunately the value of money had declined sharply since he had made his will. He had also spent a good deal with a charlatan inventor who had persuaded him it was possible to breed a strain of living fish finger. Now if I were to buy a horse that was a quarter, let alone halfway, decent I could keep it in training for only one of the years unless it won and I had a decent bet.

And so the fun began. First I had to find a trainer who would buy me a yearling. I did not fancy an animal that had been through someone else's yard and hadn't made the grade there. I knew, of course, that all the big yards dispose of a large number of horses in training to make way for next season's two-year-olds but a friend of mine, Hugo, had bought such a horse at Ascot sales one autumn. It had been placed twice in Ireland and had then run for a well-known Newmarket trainer in September. The horse was beautifully bred and he got it for a fair price. It was the answer to one of those racing riddles. Question: What is the difference between a two-year-old first time out and beaten in a photo-finish and ridden by X or ridden by Y? Answer: If it is ridden by Y you still have a two-year-old.

It started the next season as favourite for a maiden mile at the first mixed Ascot meeting, where it led for the first three furlongs before finishing in the pack. Not fully wound up, said the trainer. Personally, riding in the stands, I had thought it had run out of energy after a fight all the way to the start with its jockey. Two weeks later, in a panic, it broke through the stalls at Salisbury and broke a shoulder as it hit a car whilst galloping along the main road.

Hugo, who had had the three-year-old, had moved trainers after that incident and was now very happy with a man in his fifties, Tommy Blackthorp, who had a yard near Winchester and whose real passion was breeding gundogs. Not that he was any slouch as a trainer. He had a mixed yard, jumpers and flat horses and although he had never won a classic it was a rare year that he didn't win a big handicap or a Group race of some sort. We had met often enough and he said he would be happy to look out a yearling for me at the Newmarket Sales. It would be better if I came along too but if I could not make it he would be buying a few animals for his owners. I could come down when they were settled in and make my pick.

In the event I couldn't make the trip to Newmarket but I had the catalogue and Blackthorp read me out the lot numbers he had bought and the prices. He wasn't asking a premium for any of his purchases. When it came to it there were only two I fancied from the catalogue. I wanted a filly rather than a colt because I had this fantasy that if she won I could retire her and she could become a foundation mare for the imaginary stud farm I was about to found. Both the animals were well bred. Their sires had each won a Group One race and the mothers had won at least some sort of race above selling class. So that if my filly could win and had to be sold there would be some black type – denoting winning form – in her sales entry. I certainly couldn't afford the purple but they were a definite shade of lilac.

I can't pretend I had any idea about conformation but Tommy assured me they each had good bones. They were walked round but there was no real choice so far as I was concerned. Roger would never have forgiven me if I had bought the chesnut. It had four white feet and was what is called flashy and therefore supposedly ungenuine. Roger had a rhyme which he had made me learn as a child, against, I suppose, an occasion such as this.

> No white feet
> Run it for your life
> Two white feet
> Give it to your wife
> Three white feet
> Give it to your man
> Four white feet
> Sell it if you can
> Four white feet and white upon its nose
> Hit it on the head and feed it to the crows.

Over the years she turned out to be a front-running two-miler who nearly won at the Festival meeting at Cheltenham. A gamer mare you could not find. So much for Roger's ditty. I bought the bay filly.

Then came the fun, choosing colours. I wanted some that I could see from the stands, so I chose all white with a navy sash and a white cap. Then there was the name. Some, like those of previous Derby winners, were excluded. They couldn't be more than seventeen letters. Should I call her Aunt Lizzie? Perhaps that would be unlucky. What about a combination of the names of her sire and dam? No, everyone did that. Finally I decided that since I loved her I should call her Jetaime.

After that came the fun of the early morning work, watching her led out, then cantering, then working and then trial gallops on chill spring mornings with the plume blowing from the horses' nostrils. Bacon and eggs with Blackthorp and then a walk around the yard patting the horses and wishing them luck for their runs the following week. I cannot remember when I was happier.

Perhaps, by now, I should have said something of myself. I had been sickly as a child. My parents had lived in Egypt and had died within a few months of each other and I had been shipped home to my aunts. My education, supplemented as I say by Roger, was perfectly normal but for a time, perhaps a period of say a year, I 'knew' things. I never worked out, indeed I have never tried, to discover how I 'knew' nor did I try to extend my range. Indeed, because I was afraid of being mocked, I kept things very much to myself. In fact I think I only ever confided in Roger twice.

I suppose my 'knowledge' can be explained away. After all, there were only three places where Lizzie put down her glasses, so the sceptic would say the odds against a correct decision when she asked me where they were were only 2/1. Nevertheless I 'knew' that they were by the bed rather than on the mantelpiece. I knew other things too, such as the village scandal that the vicar's wife would leave him to go off with, horror of horrors, another woman. Lizzie wrote telling me of this. There was no need but I didn't like to tell her that.

What I did tell Roger was to back a horse named Flosuebarb when she ran at Plumpton. I could 'see' the Stop Press in the evening paper giving her as the winner. I woke up saying Flosuebarb a whole week before the race. I suppose it can be explained that somewhere I had read the name and because it had appealed – I recollect it was the combined name of three ladies who owned the mare – it stuck with me. But I swear I had never read it before I started to dream and think Flosuebarb. It is true that then I did start to look up the papers to find out if there was such a horse. Roger did back it and I believe the favourite fell two out when leading leaving Flosuebarb clear. Certainly she won.

Then my powers seemed to fade. Sometimes in my teens and early twenties they worked so that I 'knew' a number would come up on a roulette wheel but more often I wasn't sure and indeed I only ever 'knew' things which were financially worthwhile on a limited number of occasions. More often I 'knew' things which were totally useless. The last time I recall 'knowing' was that a blues singer in a club was going to sing, as her second song, the Bessie Smith number 'Cake Walking Babies' and I did have the sense to say to the girl I was with that this is what she would do. My status ran high for at least a week after that but when I was asked to find lost things and tell her whether her shares would be up by the end of the week, I found it had been a one-off. Accordingly I lost considerable face, but there's no way I could have known in advance what that woman was going to sing.

And then curiously with the arrival of Jetaime my powers seemed to return but in a completely non-financial way. I've always wanted to be able to look in a mirror and see the Tokyo Stock Market Index a week hence but I never had that power. All I could do were ridiculous things like saying the next three buses would be number twenty-nines. Possibly there is an explanation. One would be that number twenty-nine buses travel in convoy. So I kept my knowledge to myself.

As for Jetaime, she turned out to be a real little madam. At times I didn't love her at all. She had an opening race at Salisbury and finished a respectable seventh of twelve but next time in pouring rain at Lingfield she more or less refused to leave the stalls. Off to Warwick, where she ran in snatches, finishing fifth and doing her best work at the finish.

After that we put her in a seller in the July meeting at Newmarket one Friday evening. It's a lovely little track with none of the wide open spaces of the course proper. A seller is always a risky thing to do for after the race anyone can bid for the winner and the owner may have to pay a high price to retain the horse.

Tommy had horses down at Goodwood and didn't come up for the evening. The head travelling lad saddled her up. Eddie Fordham, who was a very decent lightweight and had been riding in India, was up. 'What are the instructions?' he asked. 'Make it all,' said the lad, and Fordham did just that. He was ten lengths clear at the distance and held on a short head. The *Sporting Life* had some fairly hard things to say about the favourite's heart: 'could not or would not go through with his effort' was among the kinder observations. I was halfway beside myself, first with excitement at having a winner and then with the worry that she would be bought if I was run up in the auction. 'It was a bloody rotten race,' said

Fordham, grinning as he took the saddle off. He was getting on and didn't get too many winners. Success could breed rides for him.

And that's what others thought about the race and Fordham. There was no bid as Jetaime lolloped around the ring with the auctioneer trying to garner some interest from the punters. 'You saw her win well tonight . . . dam's bred winners . . . ran on gamely . . . sure to win more.' But no one was convinced and after one more despairing 'Won't anyone start her off?' he said, 'Take her away,' and off she went for the trip back to Hampshire. And I went back to London in something approaching seventh heaven, listening to the late racing results on the radio. 'Newmarket, 7.15. First, Jetaime . . .' And I bought all the papers next day to see if they had anything to say about her. The *Life* had a picture of Fordham on another horse saying how, after his win last night, he could double up in the main event at Catterick that afternoon. He'd picked up a spare ride. None of the others mentioned Jetaime except in the results but I cut them all out anyway.

But whatever the lack of interest shown in her at the auction she must have shown something extra to the head travelling lad for Tommy Blackthorp said we should send her to Doncaster for a smart maiden at closing at the Leger meeting. That was for horses which hadn't won at the time the entries closed. Her win in the seller didn't count against her for weight either. There were no penalties added.

And now I began to dream about her. Now sceptics can say that I was in love with the horse, which I was, and that it was dream wish-fulfilment and so on. But the dreams as Doncaster approached became clearer. Jetaime was running on a left-hand track, which Town Moor certainly was. She was leading, which she certainly would do if she was going to win, but the dream never ended with a conclusion. Nor were my daytime thoughts clear. There was an increasing clarity in what I believed were the results of the racing from Doncaster and in the Stop Press the word Train. In my dreams I was in the paddock waiting for the jockey and watching Jetaime walk round. As far as I could tell Tommy wasn't there. As the race grew closer the jockeys walked into the paddock, the sun reflecting off their silks. Then they went to the start; then the race began. I never saw the finish. There was also an announcement over the tannoy which I couldn't quite hear. In the Stop Press I could now more clearly see that Jetaime had won at 16/1 but the paragraph under it with the word Train now included Crash.

I thought long and hard before saying anything to Blackthorp. After all I was a minor owner who was no close friend of his but as the dreams became clearer I knew that he was involved. It was clear to me there was to be a train crash and it had something to do with the race. I knew that Blackthorp had planned not to drive to the course but to catch a train from London after spending the night with some cronies at a racing club dinner. He had a couple of horses owned by a syndicate and they had invited him to a dinner. It was bound to be what is euphemistically called a heavy evening. He was a demon about not drinking and driving and he didn't fancy being over the limit the next morning. What was I to say? I knew the train would crash but which train? After all there were any number of race specials to Doncaster and not only from London. He would laugh at me anyway. I could hardly go to British Rail and say 'don't run any trains to Doncaster today, there's going to be a terrible accident'. Well-known clairvoyants and dream interpreters are not the most popular or believable of people, let alone unknown ones. I would be a laughing stock. But I 'knew' Tommy must not go on the train. And I hit on the idea that Hugo could give him a lift in his car. There was no problem: even if both of them thought it was curious that I should become the transport manager it was less absurd than my previous thoughts of shutting down British Rail for the day. I mentioned it to Hugo and Tommy accepted the lift without hesitation. The accident was avoided.

Jetaime was in the first race and I arrived at the course far too early. Tommy had been very confident she would run well. It was a lovely autumn day. He and Hugo had not arrived when I went to the pre-saddling enclosure. There was nothing unexpected in that. The traffic was bound to have been dreadful. I had been in Hull the previous night and it had been little more than an hour's pleasant drive to the course. Anyway it was really part of the dream.

The filly looked well and the head lad knew it. 'We're confident,' he said. Blackthorp's wasn't a gambling stable and I knew that a remark like that meant their money was down. So was mine. In any event I had no problem. I knew she would win and I had solved the second half of the problem. It was just a question of hoping the train accident was a minor shunt with no one hurt, and going to collect my winnings.

And so the dream unfolded. The jockeys, the sun glinting off their silks, as in a Munnings picture, came into the paddock. Life was imitating art again. Eddie Fordham had the ride again. One thing Jetaime clearly didn't like was being in a bunch with other horses and he knew his instructions were to try to make it all. 'Every furlong post a winning one,' said the head lad and Fordham grinned, showing two missing top teeth. He mounted and rode out of the paddock. Jetaime went down smoothly enough. I noted with some satisfaction she was well out in the betting. I had had £500 on her nose. This would keep her through the winter and into next season.

I went back to the owners' enclosure. I was excited but not that worried. I looked quickly for Hugo and Tommy Blackthorp but the enclosure was packed and I would meet up with them afterwards. I simply focused the glasses on the stalls. Fordham jumped out and made the running. This time, however, he was not being allowed to go clear. In fact Jetaime didn't have the speed and class to do that to a higher calibre field. She and the second favourite Malabar ran more or less neck and neck and despite my inner knowledge I worried that they might be cutting each other's throats and let in someone who had been waiting for a run on the rails.

That's how it happened. Jetaime started to roll in the last hundred yards. She had the second favourite beaten but she came off the rails and up came the favourite. It's a left hand course at Doncaster and Fordham, perhaps a trifle late, changed the whip into his right hand to keep her straight but she was tiring and the gap closed. I couldn't see the favourite being snatched up but maybe that was wishful thinking. Jetaime won by a short head.

As I was walking to the winner's circle to greet her, I could see Fordham looking grim and talking to the head travelling lad as he rode her in, touching his cap to what was muted applause. Almost simultaneously there was an announcement over the tannoy.

The Stop Press in the evening paper showed she had won at 16/1. But underneath it read 'Stewards' Inquiry'. Underneath that it read, 'Trainer killed in car crash on way to races.' The Stewards demoted Jetaime to second place and suspended Fordham for three days for careless riding.

The Amateur

SIMON RAVEN

'What about a trip to the September meeting at Perth?' I said.

'No,' said Rollo Rutupium very firmly, 'not Perth.'

'Why not? It's one of the most attractive courses in the kingdom.'

'So I used to think,' said Rollo. 'I changed my mind.'

'Why?'

Rollo thought heavily for half a minute.

'Once upon a time,' he said at last, 'I had an affair with a very appetizing undergraduate in Trinity Hall.'

'What's she got to do with it?'

'He. This was over forty years ago . . . before all those women shoved themselves in where they weren't wanted.'

'Oh, come on, Rollo,' I said. 'It must be rather jolly there now, with plenty of girls around.'

'There were plenty forty years ago, if you knew where to look. The thing was that they all had their own colleges and had to go back to them for most of the time. A man could get away from them if he wanted to. They weren't in one's room giggling and whining and demanding and wearing out the furniture all day and all night – which is what it's like now, my nephews tell me.'

'Well, that's their worry. This catamite of yours in Trinity Hall – what's he got to do with Perth Racecourse?'

'He wasn't my catamite, for a start. A catamite is a boy whom you bugger. Although I have always been in favour of widely varying sexual practice with all the genders, I absolutely drew a line at buggery. Messy, painful, and (as it now turns out) potentially lethal.'

'All right,' I said, 'this fancy boy of yours. What's he got to do with Per – '

'He wasn't a fancy boy either. Definitely not mincing or dainty. He was butch and wholesome and just a little bit bandy. Played cricket and rugger for Trinity Hall. Blue eyes and Viking blond hair and a slightly snub nose. Medium height. When he played tennis in white shorts, his bonny bow legs (smooth as silk) used to flash and twinkle all over the court like magic.'

'Steady on,' I said, 'that's enough.'

'No, it isn't,' said Rollo. 'If you want to appreciate this story, you must first know all about Micky. Micky Ruck, he was called. I sat next to him by accident in one of Professor Adcock's lectures on the late Roman Republic. Adders was buzzing away about that crook Clodius, and suddenly there we were, Micky and I, playing footsie and kneesie and thighsie like a pair of demented fourth formers . . . Mind you, I was quite a dish myself in those days. Tall and languid and sinuous . . . hardly a hair anywhere on my body, except a small blob of pert pubes.'

'Love at first sight?'

'No love about it. Sheer randiness. Yearning for flesh and skin. But there *was* affection. I enjoyed his sort of accommodating naivety, while he admired my upper class demeanour and cynicism. So in no time at all we were lusty bedfellows – he used to laugh a lot, I remember, just before he came – and excellent occasional companions, playing squash and watching cricket at Fenner's. However, there was just one cloud in the sky.'

'Scandal?'

'No. We usually met in my own college, King's, and in King's in those days nobody worried about that kind of carry-on. However, the trouble was that Micky was afraid that because he liked doing it with other boys he might turn into a full-time homosexual. The Classics master at his school, unlike the Classics master at mine, hadn't pointed out to him that the norm both in Greece and Rome, at any rate among the best people, was an easy-going bisexuality. So I now made this plain to him, quoting chapter and verse, and just to set his mind at rest I arranged for my cousin, Heather Sopworth of Girton, to give him a go. As I told you just now, you could always find a girl if you needed one, even then . . . long before they infested the entire University.'

'And how did he get on with Heather Sopworth?'

'Spiffing. Heather was a grand girl, as I knew well enough; we'd been intimate playmates since we were twelve. She told Micky that he was the best she'd ever had except me, and explained that a taste for boys made boys far more attractive to girls (jealousy and curiosity) and also made girls far more attractive (by sheer contrast) to boys. He could have the best of all possible worlds, she told him, but he should remember that he had only a limited time in which to enjoy them: boys will be boys, but not for long. When he became a man, she said, he'd probably still be pretty attractive, but by then women might expect him to be faithful to them, or even to marry them, and that would be a bore. So gather ye rosebuds while ye may, Heather urged, on both sides of the garden path.'

'I still don't see,' I said, 'what any of this has to do with Perth.'

'Patience,' Rollo said. 'So Micky was gathering rosebuds in all directions, Heather's and mine and God knows who else's, when it occurred to me one May morning that I should be going down for good in June, after which I should have National Service for two years, much of it very likely abroad, and that there would be an end of Micky Ruck. I therefore decided to extend my stay in Paradise by arranging a last spree with Micky the following August and September, before he must go back to Cambridge and I myself must list for a temporary lancer. Micky and I would have a Grand Sporting Tour, taking in Festival Cricket Weeks – there were plenty of those then, before the game was put in the charge of a money-grubbing inquisition from the Corporals' Mess – and lots of tennis tournaments, both real tennis and lawners, and plenty of golf and racing. We could start at Lord's, make our way up through England and then Scotland to Gleneagles, and then on to the goal and crown of the whole expedition, the September Meeting (here we are at last) at Perth.'

'Bravo,' I said.

'One possible obstacle, however, was Micky's adoring mum, who liked her little boy to be with her during the hols. Luckily she was a howling snob. I hadn't inherited then but she knew who I was, so to speak – Micky never really understood all that, bless his heart – and she was very pleased with our friendship. As for the idea that "something" might be going on, it didn't bother her. She wasn't fussy. I did have to pay a toll of a night in bed with her – but it was no trouble. Like her son, she roared with laughter when she was coming; and she kept on calling me "Micky darling" by mistake, which had interesting and rather exciting implications. Anyway, I soon had her imprimatur for our journey.

'And so off we went, Micky and I, in that Lagonda I used to have, playing in the odd match for the Butterflies and IZ – Micky belonged to neither but a few smiles at the right people soon settled that problem – watching the late county games, going to early National Hunt meetings at Hereford and Stratford and Sedgefield (proper country meetings, none of those pimply pimps and lacquered whores that you get at the meetings near London), popping in at Doncaster for a bit of Flat, di-da, di-da, some tennis (Royal) at Chester and some Shakespeare in Edinburgh, until at last we came to Perth, where we put up at a very decent pub in the forest some miles north of the course.

'We had a day spare before the racing started, and so, since Micky was getting into one of his periodical states about being too queer – he'd been laughing like a satyr all the way from London and was afraid he was enjoying himself too much – I took him to see Penny Pertuis, a busy widow whose husband had been in the same regiment as my father. Penny was a versatile lady, who now taught anthropology at the University of St Andrew's; she showed us round the golf course as far as the ninth, where we retired into the bushes for a picnic followed by a tremendous three ball. I let Micky do most of the actual fornicating, to restore his confidence, and what with him laughing and Penny bawling obscenities, which was her way of showing gratitude, I thought we'd have the entire Committee of the Royal and Ancient charging down on us like a squadron of the Greys. But no, we were only spotted by a red-headed Scots laddie looking for lost balls to sell, who happily made up a foursome – nothing so rorty as a wee ginger Scot.

'Blissfully tired after a long day in the fresh air, we set out back towards Perth, taking Penny, who had decided to come to the races with us the next day. We telephoned the pub to book her in and order our dinner, and on the way back we paid a visit to the Palace at Scone. Although the place had just closed when we reached it, Penny knew a private way in. In any case the purpose of our call was not to see the Palace itself but to inspect a remarkable graveyard they have there, in the woods near the Chapel, because Penny the Anthropologist had some theory about eighteenth-century burials in that part of the world and she had heard that there might be something helpful there at Scone.

'Now, Penny's theory had to do with the sepulchral use of the obelisk. There was, so they said, a particularly fine obelisk at one end of this very grave ground, an obelisk which had been put up over the remains of one Purvis Pride, the eldest son of Purvis Pride the Pride of Birnam – the Prides, then as now, being great men in the county and devils for hunting. The Pride under the obelisk had been killed steeplechasing in 1789, at the age of nineteen . . . this during a cross-country race, which had started in the hills up at Belbeggie and ended (so Penny told us) at a tavern which then stood by a copse in the middle of the meadow that formed the centre of the modern circuit. Young Purvis, when well in the lead, had broken his neck at the last obstacle of all – the stream in which the good woman of the tavern did her washing. She'd hung a huge nightshirt out on a hedge to dry, and the wind had got up and blown it straight on to horse and rider, blinding them both just as they were about to jump the steeply banked stream. The horse, a stallion called Jupiter Tonans, had perished with Purvis and was buried with him.

'Penny's theory,' Rollo went on, 'was that obelisks were reserved for the remains of gallant men – soldiers and sailors, explorers and adventurers. What she wanted was to read the inscription on the Pride obelisk, which was said to include a phrase which would explain why Purvis Pride, a mere local huntsman and stripling amateur jockey, had been allowed the full funereal apparatus of a proven man of action.

'Having climbed a bolted postern in the wall, which ran parallel to the Perth–Balmoral road, we approached the burial ground through graceful conifers and along a sunken path. This opened out in a delta at the east end of the cemetery, where the trees gave way to the ranked monuments. Although evening had not yet fallen, the grave ground in front of us (about one hundred yards by fifty) was diffusing its own shade of subfusc illumination from the lolling mounds and crumbling pedestals, the black slabs and sweaty cylinders, which made up the assembly of seventeenth- and eighteenth-century sepulture. We filed through the stones, Penny leading, Micky and I, seeing as little as possible of the spikes and balls and skulking crosses, until we came to the far end, the end nearest the Chapel (which was just visible through high bush and ladybirch) and the Palace itself, about a furlong beyond, on the far side of a broad, trim lawn. But our attention was soon distracted both from

Chapel and Palace by the grave, which we had come to see. A marble obelisk, of a tall man's height and topped by what looked like a mortarboard without its tassel, stood on a small grass island, which was surrounded by a moat of dark water about seven foot wide.

'"Apparently it's quite deep," said Penny, "not for wading. And anyone that jumped it would break his napper on the obelisk. Luckily I can read the inscription from here with my race glasses."

'She took these from their case . . . the ones her husband had used all through Italy.

'"Take it down," she told me, and glinted through the glasses at the inscription on the side of the obelisk, which was facing us.

'" 'Brave rider, Purvis Pride', " she read, " 'brave stallion had to ride; *Jupiter Tonans* him did call, who slew both by cursed fall.' Not a high standard of verse," observed Penny. "But there's a bit more – in Latin. *'Nonne quidem stuprorum poenitet animum equitis hic sepulti in saecula saeculorum cum nobilitate equi sui?'* Interesting use of the abstract: 'the nobleness of his horse' instead of 'his noble horse'."

'"In sum," translated Micky, looking over my shoulder at the transcript, " 'surely the soul of the horseman repents of his *stuprorum* – debaucheries – buried here as he is for ever with his noble horse?' Informing us that the horse, *Jupiter Tonans*, is in there too."

'"That we knew," said Penny, "though it is useful to have it confirmed. The glowing tribute to *Jupiter Tonans* obviously explains why Purvis Pride's tomb was dignified with an obelisk. Clearly the obelisk is for 'the noble horse' rather than his rider. But there remains a slight mystery: it seems that Purvis was guilty of certain *stupra* of which, it is hoped, he will repent at leisure, perhaps influenced in this by his 'noble' companion. Evidently these *stupra* were considered no great matter; otherwise this memorial would not have been allowed an obelisk in the first place however great the fame and nobility of *Jupiter Tonans*. The nice question is, *exactly* what were they, these *stupra*? Micky has translated them as 'debaucheries', but what specific debaucheries?"

'"The word is commonly used both in Latin prose and verse," said Micky the classicist, "of any sexual misdemeanour and in particular of orgies or adulteries. Perhaps Purvis Pride junior went round tumbling the local wives? Not much of a crime for a well-connected young man in the eighteenth century."

'"A considerable crime in Scotland," said Penny. "The Kirk would not have stood for it . . . and would certainly not have permitted him this kind of interment in this kind of place."

'"No doubt," I myself put in, "Father Pride the Pride of Birnam had a liberal palm for greasing other palms. Come to that, the Kirk or the episcopalians – whichever administrated this place – might not have been too keen on a bloody great stallion being permitted Christian burial."

'"Good point," said Penny "A nice fat bribe covers the difficulties all round. No doubt Father Purvis squared it for both of them – for *Jupiter Tonans* and for little Purvis."

'"It would still be amusing," said Micky, "to know precisely what he squared in the way of *stuprorum*." He stooped down and looked into the black moat. "Purvis Pride, Purvis Pride," he intoned, "what naughtiness did *you* get up to?"

'Answer came there none, except for Penny's comment: "Pretty boys should not go close to still waters. Remember little Greek Hylas, who was hauled in by the water nymphs."

'"They don't have water nymphs in Scotland," Micky said, "the Kirk would never allow it."'

'The next day,' continued Rollo, 'we all went to Perth races. The course, as you know, is not far from Scone; indeed, if you stand by the second jump out from Tattersall's you can see a bit of a rampart or whatever through the trees which separate the circuit from the Palace gardens. So here we came and stood for the big race, a very long steeplechase during which the horses and their riders would take this fence three times.

'"You will observe," said Penny as we walked across the meadow from the Enclosure, "that the Purvis family is well represented. Purvis Pride – surely a descendant – is to ride his gelding, Long John Silver. Black and White halved with Black Cap."

'"Same colours as the Hall," Micky said. "Trinity Hall," he explained to Penny, "my college. We call it the Hall for short."

'"So I surmised," said Penny.

'"Of course I've backed him," bubbled Micky. "The layers gave me a hundred quid to a tenner."

' "Extravagant boy."

' "It's well worth a tenner," Micky said, "just to be standing here in this lovely place."

'One quite saw what he meant,' Rollo pursued. 'In front of us, the other side of the course, were the trees up the gentle slope to the peeping Palace; behind us was the meadow and two hundred yards away the copse near which had stood the vanished tavern, by a stream that had also vanished, where the eighteenth-century Purvis Pride had broken his neck. Beyond the far end of the course the countryside idled away, pine and bracken, to a semi-circle of low hills.

' " 'What are those blue remembered hills,' " I quoted, " 'what spires, what farms, are those?' "

' " 'That is the land of lost content,' " murmured Micky, continuing Housman's poem, while a single tear ran down the left side of Penny Pertuis's nose.

' "Pay attention to the racing, boys," she said huskily.

' "They're off!"

'It cannot be said that young Purvis Pride's Long John Silver distinguished himself. Nor did his rider. A series of blunders, the first of them at the fence by which we were standing, soon put him a good twenty lengths behind the rest of the small field (seven in all). The second time round he was trailing even further; but he managed to stay upright for a further circuit, and as he went past us for the third and last time he appeared to be rallying slightly and drawing nearer to the pack of six horses in front. When the field emerged from behind the copse, with half a mile to run, Long John Silver had come level with the last horse and seemed to be making good ground. Over the last ditch, with two plain fences still to jump, he was lying fourth . . . but thereafter reverted to his previous form, sagged back to the rear of what was now a forlorn queue. Ye Banks and Braes, the only mare in the race, was going to win by a corridor: Long John Silver passed the post last by thirty lengths.

' "So much for my tenner," said Micky; "boring race."

' "I don't know," said Penny. "For a time he quickened rather bravely. Then something took the heart out of him."

' "I don't think there was ever much heart there."

' "He seems to be showing a bit more now," Penny said.

'And indeed, having barely flopped past the post, Long John Silver with Purvis on his back in his black and white colours had started to gallop again and was coming very fast round the bend and towards the fence at which we were still standing.

'"He's riding very long," said Micky. "I didn't notice that before."

'"Perhaps he's lost his stirrups," I said.

'"No," said Penny. "He's riding long." She concentrated through her glasses as horse and jockey drew closer. "And he isn't riding Long John Silver," Penny squawked, "he's riding a stallion, dear Jesus – "

'The stallion veered to its right, jumped the rails between the course and the meadow, set straight at us, came swiftly closer. The rider, a wedge-faced youth with a shapeless black cap and no helmet, lent down and across, seized Micky by the scruff of his jacket, tensed and hauled him up like a circus act. He wheeled his horse (Micky now being bunched in front of him like a parcel), jumped back on to the racecourse, then over the hedge on the far side, and galloped away through the scattered clumps towards Scone.

'"Now we know," said Penny, shivering and jerking, "what form Purvis Pride's *stupra* took. The dead Purvis Pride. I told Micky he shouldn't have looked into that moat. You see what's happened?"

'"I think so," I retched. "It must have cost the Pride of Birnam a pretty penny in bribes to arrange for that monument – if his son's tastes were known when he was living."

'"They must have been known. *Stupra*. Abomination. Perhaps they thought he would be . . . safer . . . in consecrated ground. Perhaps they forced his father . . . to add an obelisk to keep him down . . . a moat to keep him in . . . just in case, they thought. Just in case."

'"What now?" I said. "Shall we go to the graveyard?"

'"No point," Penny said. "We can't compete . . ."

'Nevertheless we did go there. And saw nothing we had not seen the day before. The waters of the moat were dark and still as ever. We went back to the pub – what else could we do? – and ordered dinner.'

'Halfway through dinner,' said Rollo, 'Micky came back. He was shrivelled and yellow and taut. He ate ferociously, and didn't talk till he had finished. Even then he spoke mostly in monosyllables, at once clear, courteous and impersonal, as if he did not know to whom he was speaking, as if he were the voice of an answering machine. He named neither of us and made no reference to what had occurred, beyond saying, "I am there. We must go to me there. You must take me to me."

'"Now?" asked Penny.

'"Tomorrow," stated what was left of Micky Ruck.

'And so the next morning we took him there to him. We called his name. Poor, shrunken Micky leant over the moat, while Penny and I stood discreetly just behind him. "Micky, Micky Ruck," Micky called. His reflection appeared in the dark water, the reflection of a rosy, laughing boy with blond hair and a snub nose, full of jollity and juice.

'"Micky, Micky Ruck," Micky called.

'But the reflection laughed the more, waved happily, and faded.

'"Please take me away," said Micky to Penny and me, as if he were addressing two complete strangers and asking for a lift.

'And now you know,' said Rollo Rutupium, 'why I shall not, if you will kindly excuse me, be accompanying you to the September meeting at Perth.'

The Anglo-Russian Steeplechase Challenge 1990

REG WHITEHEAD

Russia's answer to Martin Pipe, champion trainer Mahmoud Tokov, had a dream. It was to have a runner in our Grand National – what else? Not surprising then that he readily accepted an invitation from Helen Scott, the editor of *Riding Magazine*, to the 1990 event.

Tokov, a Karachai, spent his youth high in the Caucasus Mountains on a stud farm, later becoming the breeding manager. There the mares run the hills with their stallion and woe betide the wolf or uninvited man who disturbs his harem. Death of both man and beast are recorded. So incidentally is 100 per cent fertility.

Summertime finds Tokov down in the foothills at Pyatigorsk, the second largest racecourse in Russia, 1200 miles southeast of Moscow. There he will train his racehorses from the Karachai Stud Farm, along with other trainers from local farms lucky enough to be able to stable and race on the picturesque course from May to September.

The literal translation of Pyatigorsk is 'five mountains'. Well named! Its central point is the informal racecourse with an ornate stand built in the 1850s and, like most things Russian, in need of renovation.

Our trip to Pyatigorsk came about when Marcus Armytage, winner of the 1990 Grand National on Mr Frisk, was approached by Tokov at Aintree shortly after his memorable triumph. The invitation was extended with promises of 'some good Russian hospitality'. How could it be resisted?

With sponsorship from the *Daily Telegraph*, and promises of articles, a team of three was assembled. Jockeys Andy Orkney, Simon McNeill and Marcus Armytage set off for Moscow along with me, acting as team manager.

The Bigar Hotel in Moscow is situated alongside Moscow's race-course, The Hippodrome, and throughout the summer months is inhabited by trainers, jockeys, lads, lasses – along with racing's other, less desirable rogues. The advantage of your 5 a.m. alarm being the noise of the first lot trotting below your balcony was easily outweighed by cockroaches sharing bathroom and wardrobe.

Cheap Russian hotels are like something from another world, and, for the sake of Anglo-Russian relations, best not described – except to say that we were happy that we heeded the good advice to take a bath plug! A bath, yes. Hot water, yes. Plug, no.

The racecourse is within a couple of miles of the centre of Moscow and is used by both flat horses and trotters. Orlov trotters, named after an early breeder, one Count Orlov, are extensively used along with French, Scandinavian and American imports.

The grandstand, with its painted ceilings and 1850s architecture, must have been magnificent in its heyday. The dramatic statue of chariot and horses adorning the top of the stand overlook the five oval dirt tracks of the course. Two are used exclusively on race days, the others being for training, which starts at first light and lasts until mid-afternoon.

We managed half a day's sightseeing before we went south. Moscow's Red Square was predictably red, much redder in the sunlight than expected. The sixteenth-century St Basil's Church with its hodgepodge of multicoloured towers and cupolas is extraordinarily striking. Against a backdrop from the east of the monolithic Kremlin wall, and from the west of ramshackle rebuilding work draping Moscow's legendary GUM department store, St Basil's should look lost. On the contrary, to the onlooker's eye it dominates its neighbourhood.

The now, alas, defunct changing of the guard in front of the Kremlin, so precise, quick and smart one could be forgiven for asking them to 'Just do it once more, please.' In a blink the two replacement guards are frozen in place for their hour of guarding their country's past. No wonder, then, that this was a high spot on most tourists' things-to-do.

We had been met on our arrival at the unspeakably dreary Sheremetyevo International Airport by Dr Mikhail Alexeev, who did his veterinary training at Cambridge and thus speaks almost flawless English. 'Mischa', as he became within minutes of our meeting, was to be our guide, interpreter and guardian angel for the next ten days. It is said that no man is indispensable – not so Mischa.

The minivan driving in from the airport to our hotel passed the giant replica of a tank-trap either side of the road, some thirty feet high. A memorial to those who died almost fifty years before in the battle for Moscow, it marks the exact spot at which the German Army had been stopped, a spot not ten miles from the centre of the city. How close they came – how long the memories of them. The fresh flowers strewn about its base gave us our only solemn moment of the trip.

Our first morning found the boys eager to try out the Moscow thoroughbreds at the Hippodrome and no end of invitations were extended to 'compare the quality'.

'Would Marcoos please tell Georges what he thinks of this one and that one?' Georges, beneath his unshaven smile, doesn't look like a trainer, but he is. Aged somewhere between fifty and sixty, he wears an old suit and a week of stubble on his face, a flat hat with a large peak on his head and a cigarette butt between his silver teeth. He is a man of the south. A man of Georgia. He is also the leading flat-race trainer at Moscow. Appearances count for little in Russia. Andy and Simon were collared by other trainers keen to know their opinions, and only exhaustion brought the morning's work to a conclusion.

Back at the hotel we sampled our first breakfast: hard-boiled eggs, ham and cake, washed down with delicious steaming tea, into which we were invited to mix strawberry jam. The bottle of vodka must surely be for Mischa and Georges. Not so. Half a dozen speeches of welcome, good luck and goodbye, each ending with a mandatory toast of vodka. A way had to be found to refuse the stuff and not offend – and urgently. The Russian word for 'just a little' sounds like 'chou-chou' but – unlike the vodka – it has no effect.

We are flying to the south, having declined the train journey of thirty hours since there have been warnings of Georgian bandits working the train. They break into the compartments at night and are liable to do all sorts of unsavoury things. Travelling Aeroflot is only marginally safer, it seems.

The internal flights are loaded from the tarmac and thanks to Mischa we foreigners get preferential treatment. Having pushed our way to the steps and squeezed past a dozen petty officials we wondered if Mischa's instructions to 'sit down, do not move for anybody' did not seem unnecessarily extreme. The dark Mongolian-looking gentleman trying his best to evict Andy and Simon may have been fooled by the calm exteriors they presented, but not me. However, no one sits tighter than a steeplechase jockey, so all was well.

Eventually we were loaded with only three or four extras who, having flatly refused to get off, were herded towards the rear of the plane, presumably to stand. Not unknown, we were assured, in fact quite common.

We were not prepared for the welcome extended to us on our arrival at Pyatigorsk, where we seem to have been met by everyone, including the racecourse director, Nikolai Koleshnikov, and the smiling female manager, Larissa. 'Smiler', we later admitted, was our pet name for Larissa, only to find that she has been known locally as that for years. A smile has no national barriers.

A quick trip to the track before dinner for the boys to walk the course. At last, with the reality of seeing the fences face to face, the situation began to sink in. Certain similarities with British steeplechase tracks could be drawn. As at Aintree, the largest fence is called The Chair, and a very big fence it is too, with a large open ditch in front of a stout hedge. Other obstacles included an inviting hurdle as the first, a water jump off the top of a ramp, a brick wall, a ditch and an in-and-out consisting of two hedges.

The figure-of-eight steeplechase course is inside the harrowed dirt of the flat track, which is used solely on race days – every Saturday and Sunday during the season.

Riding out the next day, Saturday, began at sun-up, with the boys in great demand at the track where all two hundred horses running at Pyatigorsk are kept from May to October. The team were conspicuous in jodhpurs, body protectors and crash helmets. Their Russian counterparts are usually bare-headed. Safety appeared no more a priority of the racetrack than on the local roads and our driver, a veritable Nigel Mansell, left us in some doubt on which side of the road he was supposed to drive.

The horses generally held no fears for the boys, lacking a little speed maybe, but in superb condition, and with marvellous temperaments despite all being full horses.

The big day dawned with the lads getting more on edge. They

were to ride in two steeplechases, but no hurdle races. Hurdlers in Russia tend to run off flat-race weights.

Fully kitted out in their colours the Russian riders turned up at the course on bicycles – in marked contrast to their Mercedes-driven British counterparts. The team, having changed into their silks, were paraded in front of the grandstand for the draw to decide who should ride which animal – all state-owned in 1990.

First the national anthems were played, ours on an old 78 we had been asked to bring with us, under the inevitably upside-down Union Jack.

The draw, which could not have been more fair, took place in front of the smiling, 10,000 strong crowd in heat which was well into the nineties. Like *Opportunity Knocks*, the louder the cheer greeting each selection the greater its winning chance. By the sound of things two of the Russians had drawn well. However, Nikolai, a moustachioed Cossack, received sympathetic mutterings which appeared to be 'bad luck'.

Formalities over, the jockeys had to weigh out. This was done on antiquated scales under a tree in the paddock. The Clerk of the Scales was a very pretty girl with an enchanting smile – and, at whose request I am not saying, joined us for dinner that evening. Don't think that all Russian women look like lady shot-putters!

Andy Orkney's first ride was a grey, which did a good impression of a circus horse. He entered the paddock with tail bolt upright and proceeded to flip over backwards whilst being saddled. Its trainer had wanted Orkney to lead the horse to the start. Andy, quite rightly, stolidly refused. Simon and Marcus had received similar instructions on how to handle their mounts, both of which included 'Ride them hard at The Chair or pay the consequences...'

The first race went as predicted. The Russians on their two fancied mounts went ahead, and Marcus, on the big bay stallion Galit, jumped The Chair from a near standstill after plenty of urgings. Simon's mount broke down approaching the water, and, after performing miracles to stay in the saddle, he was forced to pull up.

Andy's half-breed, which had behaved impeccably once saddled, began to drop out after the first circuit. The result: a Russian one and two, with Marcus third and a gallant Andy plugging on to finish fourth. Galifax came home the winner under Magomed

Tokov rather as the crowd had predicted. A pause for breath, and to let the sweat run beneath the body protector, and off again.

In the second steeplechase, a mile and seven furlongs, things were to be different. A nasty incident occurred before Andy Orkney's memorable triumph on Altan. The tactical riding of one of the Russians – worth at least a fourteen-day suspension over here – caused a carve-up of his five rivals just after the fourth fence.

In fact, he caused more trouble for his compatriots than for the British team, who avoided the trouble created by his undisciplined antics. Nikolai, the local hero, failed to complete yet again.

The reception for Andy Orkney was rapturous, as indeed it was for the whole British team. The crowd greeted us with wide smiles, gold and silver teeth on show everywhere, and their enthusiasm made the more obvious by the way they hugged the jockeys. Mischa had to forcibly rescue Andy after his victory from the clutches of a male admirer, who had all the appearances of 'having staked his last rouble'. Orkney looked like a babe in his arms.

Simon and Marcus, at least, kept behind the rail separating the track from the stands, signing autographs for the many newfound fans among the stench of Russian black tobacco – seemingly everyone smokes.

After some pretty liberal arithmetic the scores were level and the Olympic Code of Honour – that it is not the winning but the taking part – was never more appropriate. Friendship rather than rivalry had won the day, and it was the perfect result.

Before we all left the track some two hours later many toasts were drunk, not only in vodka but also champanski, the name for the locally produced champagne. The region is famous for its mineral waters and their beneficial effects. Let us say very firmly that they are an acquired taste. In 1990 there was no beer available, no Coke, no Fanta and no Pepsi. What despair when we entered the night club and found that the cans were empty and for display only!

The party thrown later that evening was held in a large, over-ornate room, with a live Russian group playing both Western pop and ethnic music. The team gave a great account of themselves with their efforts at Cossack dancing. The Russian rider Nikolai Amelchenko put on a thoroughly professional performance and showed just how much strength is needed in the lower limbs. All of us had been split up and placed between non-English speaking

Russians, but communication just flowed. Who needs language at a time like that?

Next day we were collected from our unexpectedly new and comfortable accommodation. Its holiday-like quality was explained by the fact that it was a holiday camp during the summer months.

Once inside the minivan we were soon reminded by the heat that we still had not found a method of saying 'no' to the vodka. We set off into the mountains and our first port of call was the original stud farm of the Karachai whose legendary hospitality had gone before them.

A parade in the stallion arena of their top horses showed that they kept their horses in perfect condition. The talk of poverty, and indeed the visibility of it in Moscow, was not evident here either in the people or their animals. A son of Mill Reef and relative of their famous horse Anilin, and several of lesser blood, were paraded for us prior to the lunch.

A sheep had been killed at sun-up in our honour, and boiled in large pots reminiscent in size and looks to something Shakespeare had dreamt up for the witches' scene in *Macbeth*. The table groaned beneath the food: there was every type of local veg from the obvious tomatoes, pickled cucumbers and onions to lesser-known herbs and lettuces, yoghurt, caviar, salted carp – bred on the farm – and exotic fermented mare's milk, koumiss. There could be no way we could possibly do justice to our hosts. However, we were assured that 'this is the way it is in Russia'.

Steeplechase jockeys are a breed of their own when it comes to courage. They take the bruises and the breaks uncomplainingly and get back up from the ground without a murmur. I am their greatest admirer. Appetites they do not have. An ability to try the unusual they do not possess, and the fermented mare's milk, an essential aid for the digestion of the boiled lamb, was for them the last straw.

Unimaginably large pieces of sheep were distributed to the all-male gathering and mostly eaten with fingers. The mantle of guest of honour had fallen on my shoulders, which simply meant that it was to me that they looked for the replies to the endless toasts. By the time I had toasted the stud, its director, the horses, and to building bridges of understanding, the pulverizing effect of the vodka was taking its toll and all hope of originality finally departed.

Mischa banged the table for silence and Vladimir rose to his feet.

A faithful servant of the stud farm for forty-five years, we were told, with his crew-cut hairstyle and wizened features he might have seemed frightening were it not for the broad grin permanently worn from ear to ear. The Karachai believe he has mystical powers.

He called for the shoulder blade of the sheep, now devoid of its flesh, and poured vodka into the socket and toasted the assembled company. He then held it to the light to read the fortunes of all of us. Pretty impressive – and pretty convincing if the silence accorded to him was anything to go by. Mischa assured us good fortune was predicted, which was just as well. The reading ended with a flourish, and a loud snap of the bone to seal in the luck.

If there was a sobering thought it was that here we were, honoured to be the first Englishmen to be entertained by the Karachai for perhaps seventy-five years or more, and certainly the first to race against our opponents since the Revolution.

The meal over and our goodbyes having been said, we headed even deeper into the Caucasus Mountains through stunning countryside – a mixture of the Alps and the Rockies – onwards and upwards to our hotel, which was a concrete monster set in what has to become a future Zermatt. Snow-clad even in summer, the mountains climb up to the sky and glacial streams pulsate past the windows and crash down to the lakes below – pure magic in a land which has escaped the pollution of our misused world, and where the grass has every kind of flower and long-forgotten herb growing in profusion – a reminder of 'what was' in England's green and pleasant land. No wonder this region is the centre of the horse-breeding industry, where the foals do so well in their early life.

Here the Arab studs produce some of the most sought-after and best-bred Arab horses in the world. The Tersk Stud Farm exports its progeny through Holland, where large prices are not unusual. Indeed, in 1981 the Tersk sold Pesnyar for a million dollars at international auction. Blood lines from horses originating near here can be found the world over.

Other Russian breeds such as the Budyonny, the Don, the Kabardin, the Tersky are all bred down south in large numbers, as is the long-backed Akhal-Teke with its strange markings, and frequently copper colouring, so intense in strong sunlight. This land is, after all, just north of Turkey.

Our last day before the mad dash back to Pyatigorsk and the

vagaries of Aeroflot, and we are whisked to one of the highest peaks of the district by a chair lift, which performed flawlessly, though the lack of even the most rudimentary safety equipment was a bit daunting. It proved worth the risk to see the full magnificence of our surroundings. One day someone is going to exploit the tourist possibilities, but even civilization will have a hard job to ruin this.

Simon McNeill summed it all up in his one and only toast when he said: 'In all my life I have never enjoyed myself so much with my clothes on!' He spoke for us all.

I am happy to say that we were able to invite the Russians back to ride in England on three separate occasions, and other British teams returned to Pyatigorsk in 1991 and 1992. The latter year – a near-catastrophe when all the English fell, Carl Llewellyn ended up in hospital, Luke Harvey broke his collar-bone and Marcus Armytage tore the ligaments in his knee – is another story.

A Horserace Made in Heaven

TONY MORRIS

'Well, sir, have you made your choice? On which will you care to wager?'

The words aroused me from my reverie, and as I turned to face the questioner, up went his top hat, exposing a shock of thick fair hair over a strikingly patrician face. The aquiline nose, the bushy eyebrows, the neat side-whiskers, the slightly condescending smile expressed by languid eyes, here was the perfect example of Victorian nobility in its prime. I recognized him instantly, of course, but in my surprise at encountering him I was too slow to make the polite response.

'Henry Rous, Admiral Rous,' he offered, along with his hand, not so much correcting himself as providing further information, if it had been needed. No such need existed, and I ventured some platitude about being pleased to meet him as I accepted the cordial handshake of the man who formulated the Rules of Racing, who spent most of the next three decades ensuring that everyone observed them, and who, throughout that time, held the reputation of being the greatest handicapper that the Turf had ever known.

In his day he was often called an autocrat, and a lot worse besides, but one and all respected him as the finest judge of form, of racing, and – not least – of the people in the sport. He made enemies easily, usually of villains, but occasionally, as he grew older, merely of people whose point of view he failed to see. He outlived the era in which he belonged, and in that respect at least he was not unique.

Yet here he was no crotchety old buffer, but instead an upright figure of impressive physique, dignified, but clearly capable of turning on the charm. Somehow it did not seem odd to find him in the prime of life. But then it also did not seem odd that only he and I were around, just the pair of us standing by a racecourse paddock, gazing on a sight that millions were dying to witness.

It was not a course that I had seen before, this lush green expanse where countless varieties of tree decorated the landscape, yet nowhere obscured the view. The course was flat and fair, set between neatly trimmed hedges, while all around immaculately tended flower beds provided a blaze of colour, adding to the impression that this was the vast garden of a majestic stately home. A gentle breeze brought the scent of the flora to the nostrils, while the sun shone in a cloudless sky and an atmosphere of total tranquillity prevailed.

'Such an idyllic setting, Elysian Fields racecourse,' said my companion, adding needlessly, 'and the only possible venue for this race.' He was right, of course. Try as we might on Earth, it was never possible to bring together all the best horses of even one era; like as not, when we assembled what we reckoned was an outstanding field, some did not produce their optimum form for one reason or another, and the outcome posed more questions than it provided answers.

The going in the Elysian Fields is always perfect, and every runner is always at the peak of his or her form. Luck, of either variety, is never a factor. Better yet, that sense of timelessness is real here. The actual birthdates of the horses are irrelevant; though some may be separated by a century, they are all three year olds, and they are all impeccably prepared for the ultimate test at the classic distance of a mile and a half.

'I hope you realize how privileged you are,' said the Admiral, and though I scarcely needed convincing, he continued, 'I spent a lifetime rehearsing for this task and another hundred years or so selecting the runners. With no false modesty, I really was the only person qualified to do the job, and certainly the only man of my era to recognize that the likes of Flying Childers, Eclipse and Highflyer came far too early in the development of the breed to rank alongside the best of their descendants. In time the rate of improvement slowed and eventually, some time in the twentieth century, reached a plateau. Then, when the occasional outstanding horse came along, you never knew quite how good it was; this is where those questions are answered. They are all here.'

By now the field of twelve had left the Paddock and was being paraded for our inspection. What an impressive line-up Rous had arranged! Kincsem was the first to appear, and who could doubt her right to be here? She had run all over Europe, taking on the best in her native Hungary, as well as those in Austria, Germany, Czechoslovakia, France and England, and in fifty-four starts over four seasons in training she never knew defeat. A striking liver chesnut, with not a trace of white about her, she bore the lean look of a natural stayer, but her record said she was just as proficient at five furlongs as she was at two and a half miles and all points in between; as a three year old she had won seventeen times, including a complete set of five classics, albeit in three different countries. It was arguable that there had never been a mare to touch her for her formidable combination of toughness, class and versatility.

Next came St Simon, who was not going to win anything on looks, but whose scrawny appearance belied an awesome reputation. He had won all nine of his races, and while it might be said that he had never beaten another high-class performer at the top of his game, that was not entirely his fault. Such competition as had come his way had been ruthlessly swept aside, and his accomplished trainer Mat Dawson never doubted that none of his six Derby winners would have seen the way he went. 'My one real smasher' was Dawson's verdict, and if that plain dark bay on a dubious-looking set of limbs scarcely looked the part, the fact that he became one of the greatest sires in the history of the breed surely lent some credibility to the assertion.

A much more impressive specimen was Ormonde, another proud possessor of an unbeaten certificate. Sixteen outings yielded a like number of victories, from two years to four, the powerful bright bay establishing his claims to greatness most forcibly as a three year old, when he trounced one previously undefeated celebrity (Minting) in the Two Thousand Guineas and another (The Bard) in the Derby. Stricken with a wind infirmity before the St Leger, he nevertheless completed his Triple Crown with ease, and in the following season he set the seal on his fame with a runaway victory in the July Cup, proving himself a champion as both sprinter and stayer. His trainer, John Porter, handled other Derby winners, even other Triple Crown winners, but none he could mention in the same breath as the colt who gave Fred Archer the last of his classic victories.

Carbine provided another reminder that handsome is as handsome does. He was no oil painting even in the most flattering oil paintings of him, and here there was no disguising his want of bone, his short, upright pasterns, his weak-looking shoulder and the poor set of his head. But what manner of racehorse must he have been to win a Melbourne Cup in record time under the record weight of ten stone five pounds, conceding thirty-nine pounds to the next-best of thirty-eight rivals? He won thirty-three races in all, the first five in his native New Zealand, the rest in Australia, including a sequence of fifteen triumphs as a four and five year old. All courses and distances came alike to him, and he was, by a long chalk, the best horse to have raced in Australasia in the nineteenth century.

Next in line came two great English fillies, foaled a couple of years apart, and long renowned as the best of the Edwardian era. As she was beaten almost as often as she won – twelve times against thirteen – the impeccably bred Sceptre (by the best son of St Simon out of a sister to Ormonde) might have been considered out of her depth in this company, but alone among this illustrious group she had had to suffer from unprofessional handling. For much of her career she was trained by her owner, Bob Sievier, a man much more fitted for his other roles in life, among them scurrilous publisher, gambler and adventurer, and she was habitually ridden by jockeys whose talents never rose above the mediocre. In spite of all that, and a ludicrously conceived schedule of races, some when she was far from fit, she achieved four outright classic wins, a feat unsurpassed before or since.

If the hard bay Sceptre was a bit too long in the back and a shade too straight in her pasterns to win beauty prizes, the gleaming chestnut Pretty Polly offered a fine contrast, showing an abundance of quality and a powerful, athletic physique. Only the most captious of critics could fault her appearance, and for almost two seasons there was nothing to fault about her racing record, with fifteen wins from her first fifteen starts, as she established complete dominance over male and female rivals alike. To be sure, there were eventually a couple of defeats, but nothing to dull the impression made by her twenty-two victories, many of them by wide margins with effortless ease.

There was no mistaking Man o' War. The colt they called 'Big Red' showed awesome masculine power in his burnished chestnut frame, while the jerky movements of his sturdy limbs proclaimed his readiness, even eagerness, for competition. Here was a colt who liked to be boss, knew he was boss, and always intended to have his way. So he had, this equine fire-ball, twenty times out of twenty-one, and but for wretched luck on that sad day at Saratoga, no upstart – name of Upset – would have left that single blot on his escutcheon. Having so clearly established his dominance over his generation at two, this champion concentrated on beating the clock at three, and did so regularly, setting track, national and world records seven times from eleven starts at that age. When the cynics started to say that he kept winning for want of worthy competition, a match was arranged with the previous year's Triple Crown winner, Sir Barton; when that issue was settled with Sir Barton beaten by seven lengths and the Kenilworth track record by six seconds, the last unbelievers became converts.

The massive, coarse-looking chesnut gelding with the brushing boots on his forelegs could only be Phar Lap, who had emulated his compatriot Carbine by crossing the Tasman from their native New Zealand, and matched him in many of his achievements there as well. Overwhelmingly the best three year old in Australia, he proved better still at four, collecting fourteen wins in a row, among them a Melbourne Cup under nine stone twelve pounds. Challenged to outdo Carbine by winning it again a year later with ten stone ten pounds, he understandably failed, but he broke new ground for the Antipodean horse by venturing to America and there securing international renown with a brilliant victory in the Agua Caliente Handicap.

Now came the modern nonpareil, Ribot, the Italian who emulated no less than Caesar, coming, seeing and conquering in Britain and France. At home there was never anything to keep him warm, either from his own or preceding generations, so only by journeying abroad could he establish his true worth. He did that at Ascot (where the sticky ground dulled his performance in the King George VI & Queen Elizabeth Stakes and his jockey felt obliged to apologize for the 'narrow' five-length winning margin), and he did it twice at Longchamp, where consecutive victories in the Prix de l'Arc de Triomphe left no room for doubting his exceptional merit. At the second time of asking, when two top American horses joined the British and the French in seeking to offer resistance, he turned in nothing short of an exhibition, leaving them like a shot from a gun and rounding off a perfect career of sixteen wins from as many starts in tremendous style. He was a deceptive sort of horse to look at, showing no physical defects, but also having no features which gave him licence to be such an exceptional athlete.

Sea-Bird was another unexciting specimen to the eye, and in his case it was not hard to find faults. He was tall, leggy and relatively insubstantial in physique, not at all a quality individual, and, to boot, a darkish chestnut with stockings behind that seemed to accentuate an overall impression of gawkiness. You could not imagine what he was capable of until you saw him gallop – or rather, canter – for that is all he ever needed to do to win his Derby in what was supposed to be a competitive year. At the gallop he was even more impressive, never more so than in the Arc de Triomphe, where the strongest field ever assembled for that prestige prize was well and truly humiliated by his majestic display. His runner-up, the otherwise unbeaten Reliance, was six lengths away; there were five more lengths back to Diatome, who was to win the Washington D.C. International next time out, and strung out behind them were representatives from Britain, France, Ireland, Italy, America and Russia, all celebrities reduced to nonentities.

Only two more in the parade, and first the familiar Nijinsky, the horse who achieved what everyone said would never be achieved again. In an era ruled by specialization, he reacquainted racegoers with the merits of versatility, proving the pick of his crop as a two year old, then capturing the first English Triple Crown for thirty-five years, each jewel claimed with the peerless Piggott panache. His immediate Derby victim was the outstanding Gyr, and in the King George VI & Queen Elizabeth Stakes he cantered throughout, with his runner-up, the previous Derby winner Blakeney, floundering five lengths adrift at the finish. The St Leger brought his score to eleven out of eleven, and perhaps he should have retired there and then; instead he suffered a sensational defeat in the Arc de Triomphe and, worse still, failed to cope with the obviously inferior Lorenzaccio in the Champion Stakes. There were valid excuses for both reverses and nobody thought the worse of the big bay, whose ever-bubbling nervous energy was as conspicuous a trait as his imposing physique.

What took the eye about Nijinsky's appearance was that rugged, no-nonsense look of a hard-trained commando, whereas Secretariat was all movie idol – big and tough, certainly, but aesthetically attractive from every angle, too, superbly structured, conveying grace and power in every movement. A computer programmed with knowledge of the best points of all the best thoroughbred specimens would draw this horse; it was multimillions to one against the genes falling so harmoniously and effectively into place. Far from being just a 'looker', this masterpiece of the breed also proved a supreme athlete, first as an exceptional two year old, then as the first US Triple Crown hero in twenty-five years. His bright chestnut coat was not the only reason for his being regarded as the second coming of Man o' War, for he habitually set records, memorably in the Kentucky Derby, unforgettably in the Belmont Stakes, which he won by the phenomenal margin of thirty-one lengths.

The field was complete, and the Admiral advised a stroll to the finish line, 'for the best view of the closest contest you will ever see.' And away they charged, with Man o' War losing a little ground at the start, as he always did, and Secretariat opting for the forcing tactics that served so well at Belmont. Ribot, inevitably, lay close to the pace in company with Phar Lap, Ormonde and Carbine, while Nijinsky dropped in with Man o' War at the rear.

The pace was true and strong, Secretariat stepping it up gradually, though never with the result that he increased his advantage. On the contrary, all his pursuers maintained contact, and with none wilting under the strain, there was no bunching, no interference, no traffic problems at all; just a dozen great horses, all at the peak of their powers, delivering their ultimate performance.

Unbelievably, after the turn for home the entire field fanned out, each made aim for the target, and there was no discernible advantage to any of the various riding styles favoured by the jockeys of different eras and cultures. This was racing at its purest, the horses giving their utmost, doing it all. And as the post drew nearer, the gaps between them receded; quicker than the eye could comprehend what was happening, strides were lengthening here, shortening there, until finally, right on the line, the entire group galloped as one, quite inseparable.

'Is there no photo-finish camera?' I asked. 'No man-made devices here at all,' was Rous's response, and he elaborated, 'but it would make no difference if there were. It really was a twelve-way dead-heat. You see, everything is perfect in Paradise, and that includes the handicapping.'

'The handicapping? You mean they weren't at level weights?' I blurted out. A mischievous grin took possession of the Admiral's bewhiskered face, and the truth at last emerged. 'We have only perfect races in Elysian Fields, and it's my job, by adjusting the weights to be carried, to ensure that they happen every time. Can there be anything more perfect in racing than a dead-heat? I do hope you are not going to ask me who carried what weight in that perfect race, because it is surely better that you do not know. The runners are all your heroes and heroines. Would you really want to think less of any of them than you do now?'

He was right, I supposed. It was too much to have hoped that I might be singled out to learn the answers to the most fascinating questions that exercise the minds of generation after generation of racing enthusiasts. It mattered, too, that I should be able to preserve my illusions.

But as I drifted off with my thoughts, I could nevertheless shake my head emphatically in response to the invitation called after me.

'Are you not going to stay for the next? It's the re-match between Mill Reef and Brigadier Gerard, with Gladiateur, Citation, Nearco, The Tetrarch, Native Dancer and Shergar thrown in for good measure.' I reckoned I knew the result of that one.

The Sport of ... er ...

EAMONN PERCIVAL

The day started badly for Vince. But then every day had started badly for him over the last fortnight.

His early morning ritual usually began at around eight-thirty. His nerves could no longer bear the horror of the alarm clock and, instead, he would awaken when the morning shafts of sunlight stole across his bedroom and finally reached the floor-length mirror he had carelessly positioned diagonally opposite his bed. The effect was that of a multikilowatt spotlight trained directly at his head. One day, he promised himself, he would move the bastard but, like so many other simple tasks, it was just another item on his Things To Do When I Sober Up list and, as such, remained where it stood.

Now, what was next? Oh yeah, he had to get up and head for the bathroom where, instead of brushing his teeth, washing or shaving, his first manoeuvre was to kneel, in an almost reverent position, before the toilet bowl. Grasping the sides of the porcelain, he began to shudder and shake before finally giving in to the abdominal spasms and ejecting the contents of his stomach into the yawning mouth of Mr Shanks's finest. As he did so, he let go with a string of random expletives, all rendered unintelligible by the singular absence of consonants. Actually reaching the bathroom had been somewhat of an achievement for Vince as, over the past few months, he had turned projectile vomiting into an art form.

It was a May morning and unusually cold as he felt his way tenderly across the hallway and down the stairs. It had come as no great surprise to him to find that he was fully dressed, though his clothes were a lot more crumpled than when he had left the house nine hours earlier. Come to think of it, that was exactly how he felt. Crumpled. Dishevelled and unwashed, he was filled with the shame and self-loathing that only the veteran drunk can feel.

He had long since tired of the Never Again vow and, instead, resorted to merely murmuring, 'Fuck this for a game of soldiers,' a sentiment whose meaning he had never quite worked out – but it certainly seemed fitting for this occasion.

After two mugs of strong black coffee, Vince decided he felt man enough to tackle the basics of getting back into human shape by washing and dressing. As his head began to clear, he slowly realized that today was Saturday, a day blessed by the fact that it was not a work day and he would not have to face the unspeakable terror of Allens' print supplies warehouse, which had provided him with a reasonable source of income over the past five years in return for his storekeeping skills and – most importantly, it seemed to Vince – his attendance.

Vincent Albert Davies had made a decision many years ago that, he having reached the age of thirty-six, the world finally owed him a living and that such mundane considerations as career prospects, promotion and job satisfaction were mere avenues of futility, to be explored by others with far less imagination than he.

Yes, Vince regarded himself as a one-off. One-off the wrist, more like, most of his work colleagues would say. His total lack of interest in anything other than gambling and drinking was a constant and baffling conundrum for them.

Yet it all made perfect sense to Vince. If there really was anything more to life than betting slips and hangovers, somebody had bloody well forgotten to tell him. Even the opposite sex held no allure any more. After all, he figured, women cost money whichever way you look at it. In his experience, lavish riches and attention upon the girl of your dreams and you'll only end up with a slapped face at the end of the day. Better a drunken twenty minutes with a Dean Street whore after a result at Ladbroke's – the score at the end is the same, and at least you know where your dosh has gone.

No, there was nothing wrong with the odd flutter now and again. Where's the harm in risking a fiver here or a tenner there? It kept him off the streets and everybody should have a hobby, he reassured himself. Same with the bevy. A good night out with the lads over a pint or sixteen didn't make him a bad person, did it? There was never any trouble down the Bell, just a few old friends regularly having a good time. And what better place to pick up the odd tip for the next day's meetings? You could trust the lads when it came to track talk. Nobody would ever throw you a curve ball – after all, your win was their win and vice versa. Yep, life was sweet and on an even keel. La vita was extremely bleedin' dolce.

'Christ, it's Saturday!' he yelled out loud, remembering, with a jolt, that today was indeed something special, and not just because he didn't have to show at work.

This was the second Saturday in May, the day he had been look- ing forward to for as long as he could remember. (In truth, it was a lot longer than that, for the section of his brain labelled 'recollec- tion' seemed only to be able to stretch back a matter of hours.) It was Race Day for himself and the rest of the crew from the Bell. Today, the racetrack at Brighton was to be augmented by some twenty-two punters from Dartford, all raring to go, each one secretly convinced that today was to be the Big One.

Near-sobriety visited upon him quite suddenly and he decided there were things to do. Phil James was the only one who was sure to be up at this hour so Vince tapped out his number on his phone, after a series of false starts and accompanying profanity until he remembered to plug it back into its wall socket: he had removed it at some point last evening to ward off late-night or early-morning callers.

'Phil? It's Vince. Get your arse in gear. It's nine o'clock,' said Vince, trying (and failing) to sound as though he had been up for hours.

'I'm all packed and ready to go, you twat,' Phil replied irritably. 'I came off shift at seven this morning so I'm hardly likely to go back to bed, am I?'

Pleasantries over, they quickly worked out a list of those who would require alarm calls and who would call who. The list only included the 'real' regulars of the Bell's racing fraternity. The rest of them, or 'part-timers' as they were known, would have had to make their own arrangements for getting to the appointed meeting place at the appointed time. If they were late and missed the coach, well, fuck 'em. The ticket money had long since been collected.

The departure point was, naturally enough, the Bell, a hostelry of some repute around Dartford. Built in the early sixties on the edge of a newish housing estate, it towered over the landscape from its perch atop Cemetery Hill and was home to a fairly uniform clientele whose interests were not too dissimilar to Vince's.

Their main religion was, of course, boozing, but also high in the popularity stakes were racing, snooker and darts. Tony, the landlord, had been quick to realize the potential profit to be made from his regulars' hobbies and had just as quickly installed a giant TV screen, three snooker tables and five dartboards. Race Nights, too, were regular events at the pub, and always ensured a hundred per cent turnout.

The lads were to meet at 10.30 a.m. at the back of the boozer, where Tony was all too pleased to welcome them into the lounge bar, carefully latching the door behind each entrant after peering down the road for any sign of the local constabulary. There was hardly ever any problem with late-night or, in this case, early-morning drinking as the pub enjoyed an excellent vantage point and any uniforms could be spotted a good way off.

Vince and Phil arrived simultaneously and were ushered in towards a welcoming pint. By 10.45, everyone had arrived, by 11.15 all had slaked their thirst to the tune of a couple of pints each and, by 11.30, a happy queue was snaking its way on to the coach, which was contentedly purring away in the car park.

As the bus rumbled through the streets of Dartford, Vince sat down in the single seat across the gangway from the driver, having satisfactorily ticked off the last name on the passenger list. He allowed himself a few minutes' relaxing and sat back with only the distorted piped muzak occasionally interrupting his thoughts. The rest of the passengers consulted their copies of the *Sporting Life* or, in the case of the less dedicated, the back pages of the *Sun*.

The coach bumped on to the M25 and the ring-pulls began to fly as the bus settled into a steady 70 m.p.h. By the time they were two-thirds of the way down the A23, they were in fine voice as rousing, if not entirely in tune, choruses of 'Lily the Pink' echoed around the coach. The singing was led by Cheddar George, a West Countryman of indeterminate years who had, ever since anyone could remember, been the token life and soul of the party character among the assembled. Although it had somehow fallen upon Vince to organize the pub outings, he was quite happy to let George be the cheerleader at these events, leaving him free to open another can and continue studying form.

As the bland Surrey surroundings gave way to the more

picturesque Sussex landscape, Vince considered it was time to start thinking about the real business of the day.

'Phil, check on old Norm, wouldja mate?' he said, looking over his shoulder towards the rear seat of the coach where Sad Norm slumbered.

Phil made his way to the back and prodded the shapeless lump that was Norman Walker. The lump stirred and slowly took human form as a head appeared from the folds of a jacket at least three sizes too large for its occupant.

'Almost there, pal,' Phil informed Norm.

'Oh ... yeah ... great, great!' enthused Norm, with an expression that said otherwise. Poor old Norm, everyone said. Although he was a reasonably happy chap who enjoyed these days out, he had the unfortunate demeanour of a man who had witnessed, at first hand, all the sadness in the world. That, added to the fact that two pints of shandy would render him virtually unconscious, made him a miserable-looking specimen on the sunniest of days and earned him the epithet Sad Norm.

Phil returned to the front of the coach and reported that, all things considered, Norm was OK and that the rest of the party, suitably fuelled, was eager to get into the grounds.

Ten minutes later, the coach pulled into the racecourse car park.

At the bar, Vince and Phil were good-naturedly arguing over whose round it was. Overcome with a mutual level of generosity which only four pints or more can achieve, both insisted the round should have been theirs and that, OK, they would get the next one. They were both in a good mood. Money and betting slips had been exchanged at the windows upon their arrival and, so far, a couple of winners had just about made up for a disastrous start when, having agreed on what was surely a certainty in the 1.30, they had watched as it tried to jump a non-existent obstacle, à la Devon Lock, stumbled spectacularly, and performed a very creditable splits, all before reaching the first bend.

'Phil,' said Vince, gently nudging his drinking partner with his elbow, 'isn't that our coachdriver over there?'

Both men looked along the bar to the opposite end where, sure enough, their driver for the day was finishing off a pint with a whisky chaser whilst ordering the 'same again, squire'. His face was flushed and his collar and tie loosened. In fact, he looked as though he was already way ahead in the drinks-consumed stakes but did not appear ready to quit yet.

This did not cause Vince or Phil much concern as they had more pressing matters to deal with. Bill Randall had appeared.

'Hi boys, how's it going?' Bill asked.

Both knew he couldn't care less how they had fared so far but felt obliged to answer him.

'Oh, so far so good,' chirped Phil politely, 'early days yet mate.'

Vince glanced at Phil as, almost telepathically, a single thought passed between them. The thought was 'Wait for it, here comes the bullshit.' For William Randall was one of life's great liars. Possessing an unsurpassable talent for telling totally transparent untruths, Bill could talk bollocks for England. Known behind his back as Billy Liar, he was rapidly reaching the point of no return as his falsehoods grew more and more outrageous by the day. He would tell you his early years were spent in the army, navy or air force, which one depending either on his mood or the most recent war film he had seen on TV. All the lads from the Bell were used to this and, in fact, many derived a great deal of pleasure from deliberately setting traps in his web of lies and smiling at his heroic attempts to extricate himself.

'I'm not doing too badly so far,' offered Bill, 'probably around the four thou mark. Not bad for a £20 stake.'

'Well done, hope it lasts,' replied Vince. 'Drinks are on you then, Billy boy?'

But Bill was already walking away.

Vince unconsciously gazed down along the bar and mentally noted that their driver was no longer there. Just as well, Vince thought, we don't want our chauffeur breathalyzed.

Over the next couple of hours, the fortunes of Vince and Phil changed like the wind but at least they were sure they would not end up bankrupt on this particular occasion.

From time to time, between races and visits to the bar, they would bump into one or two of the other lads and exchange hard luck stories, the only exception being Billy who, by now, must surely be in the Super Tax league, or so he would have you believe.

As the last race was about to start, the pair were to be found back in the bar, celebrating the fact that they had entered the course earlier with £200 each and would soon be leaving showing a slight profit. By now, of course, both were beginning to see double and, glancing across the length of the bar, Vince once again recognized the coachdriver who was silhouetted against the window over-looking the paddock. He was gripping a pint glass in one hand and a scotch in the other, while teetering back and forth on his heels.

'Philip, old boy,' said Vince, wearing a slightly worried frown, 'I don't think our driver should be . . .'

He broke off as he saw the aforementioned figure tilt back at an alarming angle before crashing backwards on to a table full of glasses and rolling off on to the floor.

A phone call to the coach hire company resulted in the promise of a replacement driver and a request to dump the 'piss-artist with the peaked cap' on the back seat to sleep it off before being fired in the morning.

The relief driver arrived two hours later, by which time most of the party had re-assembled at the coach. Bill Randall had already told them that he wouldn't be there for the return journey as he would be making his way to nearby Worthing where his sister lived. Whether or not this was true, they neither knew nor cared. Either way, they would be spared another episode of Tales of Mystery and Imagination on the way back. Also missing from the coach was Norman. Nobody had seen him since the second race, but there could be no exception to the rule – not even for Norman. Those that were absent knew the penalty. Vince had told them that any stragglers or a.w.o.l. members would be considered 'missing in action' and would have to find their own way home. After all, Phil had added, Vince was the organizer and not the nursemaid and, at the end of the day, retained the right to get as pissed as the rest of them without having to worry about tucking them up in bed.

The next morning, Tony opened the doors of the Bell to three thirsty race fans.

'Morning, lads,' he beamed, beaming as only landlords can do at half-twelve on a Sunday. 'Who's the lucky bastard, then?'

Vince: 'Eh?'

Phil: 'What?'

George: 'Beg pardon, Tone?'

'The word is that one of you got lucky at the track yesterday. Who was it then?' Tony asked.

'Well, it wasn't any of us, mate, that's for sure,' said Phil.

'Nobody on the coach back, at least,' said George. 'They would have said.'

'Well, I heard that one of you lot copped for about fourteen grand,' Tony said, questioningly.

Not Billy Liar, they all thought. No, it couldn't be. Not only would he have told them he'd had a result, he would have at least trebled the amount.

They sat in silence, each alone in his thoughts, wondering who could possibly have struck lucky to the tune of fourteen big ones.

At one o'clock, the door opened and Sad Norm walked in, still looking as though he had lost his dog in a rainstorm.

'A large brandy, please,' he said quietly.

The Hermit Affair

MICHAEL CHURCH

'Lot 27, a chesnut colt by Newminster out of Seclusion . . .' A small but good-looking, dark chesnut yearling entered the sales ring. Harry Hastings and Henry Chaplin, standing on opposite sides of the ring, watched the bidding rise in fifties. Newminster, a St Leger winner, had already sired three Classic winners, including Derby winner Musjid, and his stock was commanding good prices. Harry Hastings held the bid at eight hundred and fifty guineas until Chaplin came in at nine hundred. One more bid each then Hermit was knocked down to Captain Machell bidding for Henry Chaplin, at one thousand guineas. And so at Mr Blenkiron's sale of Middle Park Stud yearlings at Eltham, Surrey, on Saturday, 17 June 1865, the rivalry between Hastings and Chaplin took a twist from which one of them would never recover.

The Sale continued . . . Lot 28, a chesnut colt by Dundee out of Shot, was sold to Mr Merry, also for one thousand guineas. This yearling, later named Marksman, was to run second to Hermit in the Derby.

Henry Chaplin was born on 22 December 1841, although some records show 1840. He was the eldest son of the Reverend Henry Chaplin, Vicar of Ryhall in Rutlandshire. When only nineteen he inherited the estate of Blankney in Lincolnshire from his uncle Mr Charles Chaplin. He went to Christ Church, Oxford, in January 1859 and was given the nickname 'Magnifico' on account of his grand life style. A year later he took the Prince of Wales 'under his wing' and before Chaplin left in December 1860 he had 'kept an eye' on a shy and nervous Harry Hastings for a term.

In 1864 he became engaged to the beautiful Lady Florence Paget, youngest daughter of the Marquess of Anglesey and 'the rage of the park, the ballroom, the opera and the croquet lawn'.

Before the engagement, Lady Florence had been courted not only by Chaplin but also by Harry Hastings, who had been her constant companion while Chaplin had been away on a big game expedition in India. On the morning of 16 July 1864, Lady Florence tried on her newly delivered wedding dress and at 10 a.m. travelled alone from the St George's Hotel in Albemarle Street for a shopping trip to the fashionable store of Marshall and Snelgrove in Oxford Street, having left a message for Henry Chaplin with the time of her expected return. After an arranged meeting with a close friend inside the store, she was quickly driven to St George's Church, Hanover Square, where she married Harry and became the Marchioness of Hastings. No members of her own family were present.

Henry Plantagenet, 4th and last Marquess of Hastings, was the classic Victorian example of a young man with plenty of money and little experience on the Turf. He was born on 22 July 1842. His father died less than two years later and this, followed by the sudden death of his elder brother in 1851, left the young Harry with a vast inheritance.

Generous and charming with friends, he treated his employees badly and when Master of the Quorn he would often quit the hunt at midday for a session of cards or dice.

And so the eternal triangle was cast. After being deserted by Lady Florence, Henry Chaplin threw himself fervently into racing, buying horses 'as though he were drunk and backing them as if he were mad!' He had, however, an ace up his sleeve. That ace was Hermit.

Under the management of Captain Machell, Hermit was trained at Newmarket by Bloss. And as time passed it became obvious that an exciting bargain was in prospect.

Hermit was first tried with a useful filly named Problem, over four furlongs on Bury Hill. Hermit beat her by two lengths, giving her thirty-five pounds. Two months later on 20 February, Problem won the Brocklesby Stakes at Lincoln, from a big field, and followed it up by beating Hippia, a future Oaks winner, at Northampton.

Captain Machell then travelled to London and backed Hermit to win the Derby for a large sum of money at odds of 20/1.

Hermit made his racecourse debut at Newmarket in the spring of 1866, where in the race before the Two Thousand Guineas he was beaten three-quarters of a length by Cellina, over four furlongs. The Machell camp were not downhearted however; Cellina had a previous victory and her experience had told. Three weeks later at Bath, Hermit reversed the placings with Cellina, winning by a neck.

In the Woodcote Stakes at Epsom, Hermit came up against Achievement, a brilliant filly who went on to win the One Thousand Guineas and St Leger the following year. She beat him by three lengths in a scintillating performance. Hermit went on to win at Ascot and at Stockbridge, where he beat Vauban again in the Troy Stakes.

Vauban was a brown colt by Muscovite out of Palm. He had won seven of his fifteen races as a two year old and the following season won the Two Thousand Guineas by two lengths from Hermit's stable companion Knight of the Garter, with Marksman a head away third.

With the Derby approaching, Captain Machell and Henry Chaplin now had a direct line to Vauban and Marksman through Knight of the Garter. A trial was arranged with Hermit giving Knight of the Garter ten pounds, over a mile. Hermit did the business and the stable's ante-post vouchers looked gilt-edged.

Soon after, arrangements were made to give Hermit a trial over one and a half miles, exactly a week before the Derby. Custance, Hermit's regular jockey, agreed with Captain Machell that Rama, a four year old who won the Doncaster Cup the previous season, should give Hermit fourteen pounds.

It was, however, decided to give both horses a rough gallop on the Monday morning, to allot the trial weights more accurately. Custance rode Hermit and after a mile was going so well seven pounds seemed the right mark. Suddenly, Hermit gave a tremendous cough and stumbled. After his nose and mouth were cleaned up Custance took him home 'the back way'. After a thorough examination at Bedford Cottage, it was discovered that Hermit had burst a blood vessel in his nostril. Later that afternoon Custance travelled to London to give Henry Chaplin a report on the day's events. After much consultation, Chaplin decided to await further developments before scratching Hermit from the Derby.

While travelling to London, Custance met Captain Hawkesley, who, surprisingly, knew of Hermit's trial. A few days later Custance received a letter from Hawkesley offering him the ride on The

Rake, the current Derby favourite. Since Custance was retained by Henry Chaplin he declined the offer. However, Mr Pryor, owner of The Rake, wrote to Chaplin, stating that The Rake was sure to win the Derby and advising Chaplin to back it, and also requesting the services of Custance. Henry Chaplin wrote back in agreement for the release of his jockey, as he did not wish to prevent Custance from winning the Derby.

Henry Custance takes up the tale from his *Riding Recollections*.

The most extraordinary part of the story is that on the Friday before the Derby, news arrived at Harpenden Races that The Rake had broken a blood vessel! That night I went over to Chantilly to ride in the French Derby, and when I returned to England on the Monday I had no idea which horse I was going to steer at Epsom. As each had broken a blood vessel, I didn't think it mattered much. On the Tuesday morning I went on to the course to ride The Rake a gallop as usual before the Derby, never having been on his back. Mr Joseph Dawson, his trainer, told me to follow some horse or other three-quarters of a mile, cantering twice, as he said his colt had done a good preparation. After I had pulled up, I said to Mr Dawson, 'Well, of all the Derby horses I have ever ridden, this is the worst!' He answered, 'Wait until you get a pair of spurs on him; you'll find him a different horse.'

On my way home I saw Bloss's horses doing their work, and Hermit was sent to canter a mile on the Derby course . . . Hermit used to pull a bit, and he got the best of the boy coming round Tattenham Corner – fairly ran away with him; and the ground being as hard as iron, he bounded over it like a cricket ball. Chris Fenning, who was standing with me said, 'Bejabers, I never saw a horse go like that! He will win the Derby.' I told him it was the first work Hermit had done for over a week, and I am afraid stopped him from backing the horse. No-one knowing what I did would have thought of doing so. Captain Machell had made up his mind to run the horse, and wished Mr Chaplin to claim me to ride him. This he did, and the matter was referred to the Stewards.

They decided that Mr Chaplin's letter to Mr Pryor constituted a release, giving the latter the right. As both horses had broken a blood vessel, they, however, thought Mr Pryor ought to waive it. This he would not do, so I had the mortification of riding The Rake, and finding my horse dead beaten coming round Tattenham Corner. At that point I saw Hermit pulling Daley out of the saddle, and I thought to myself at the time, 'How I should like to change mounts!'

Although Custance told Fleming Hermit's gallop that Tuesday was the first he had had for a week, he was unaware that Captain Machell had been working the horse in secret. Machell, having large ante-post vouchers at stake, would not give up the cause and was determined to keep Hermit's blood cool. He gave Hermit very little hay and covered him with only a light blanket. Most of his work was down-hill and, on the Saturday, Hermit did six one-mile canters the reverse way of the Rowley Mile.

Derby Day arrived, and with snow showers throughout the day, fate gave our story yet another twist – for this would surely cool Hermit's blood. His appearance in the paddock, however, was far from convincing. One observer said 'on looks he would not fetch £15 at a fair'. When the horses left the paddock Hermit's price was freely offered at 66/1. Captain Machell 'took the fractions' and topped up with a further £3000 to £45.

At the starting post the snow was falling fast, there were ten false starts and three of the jockeys were later suspended for two weeks for misconduct. When the thirty runners were finally on their way, a steady pace was maintained to Tattenham Corner. Here Vauban, the hot favourite, took up the running with Wild Moor, Marksman and Julius in pursuit. Hermit was at the rear, having been steadied. Into the straight, Vauban still led from Marksman, but Van Amburgh and Wild Moor were closing rapidly. Hermit also began to make up ground. Over the road and Marksman and Van Amburgh came alongside Vauban, the three racing together to the distance pole. Suddenly Van Amburgh was done for, Fordham was having to work on Vauban and it was Marksman who hit the front at the rising ground. Meanwhile, jockey Daley was bringing Hermit with one long run up the outside. Nearer and nearer with every stride until ten yards from the post they drew level with Marksman. In a flash Hermit's head was in front. It was over. The crowd stunned into silence or as close to silence as it ever can be on Derby

Day. The result was posted. Hermit won by a neck, with Vauban a bad third. Wild Moor and Van Amburgh followed them home.

Captain Machell was now a rich man, having won over £60,000 for his patience and determination. The stable won a further £90,000.

Captain Machell was born in Beverley in 1838 and was twenty-nine years old at the time of 'Hermit's Derby'. He had joined the army in 1855 and reached the rank of Captain in 1862. The following year he resigned his commission when refused permission to see the St Leger. He was an accomplished athlete and won many wagers for jumping from the floor on to a mantelpiece and for jumping over a billiard table. He moved to Newmarket in 1864 and after a successful start as an owner, advised Henry Chaplin to buy Hermit at the Middle Park Sales. He later won the Grand National three times within four years and was closely associated with the Triple Crown victories of Isinglass in 1893.

While Hermit's victory had brought riches to Captain Machell and Henry Chaplin, to the 4th Marquess of Hastings he had brought disaster and debts of £120,000. Hastings had laid Hermit for the Derby and fancy prices to the owner's stable for over a year, in a vendetta against Henry Chaplin. At a party on the evening of the Derby, Hastings vowed he would make the Ring settle his debts for him. The defeat of Achievement in the Oaks 'turned the screw'.

Harry Hastings arrived at Tattersalls on the Monday, having mortgaged his estates to the hilt with Padwick the moneylender and having accepted Henry Chaplin's proposal giving him time to pay. He was cheered to the man. In a gambler's world Hastings would not accept defeat; after all, his Lady Elizabeth was favourite for next year's Derby.

The year passed with mixed fortunes. Another Derby Day dawned and Harry had summoned enough credit for one enormous plunge on Lady Elizabeth. She was backed at all rates to 7/4 favourite, but was hopelessly beaten. Harry had her out for the Oaks two days later, but she disappointed again. Hastings was now totally destroyed. After a cruise upon his yacht, off the coast of Norway, he returned home to Donnington to die at the age of twenty-six. The cause of death was given as Bright's disease, brought about by excessive eating, drinking and worry. Upon his deathbed he whispered, 'Hermit's Derby broke my heart, but I didn't show it, did I?'

Florence married again, eighteen months after Harry's death. Her overtures to Chaplin had fallen on stony ground and she needed to be in the social scene. As before, her second marriage came as a complete surprise to her friends, for she married a man who was not only seven years younger than herself, but was also another highflying gambler of the Turf. His name was George Chetwynd. She had four children by her second marriage and died in 1907 at the age of sixty-four.

Hermit of course had outlived Harry Hastings and soon after his Derby victory won a Biennial Stakes and the St James's Palace Stakes at Royal Ascot.

Later he finished second to Achievement in both the St Leger and the Doncaster Cup. Although he won a small sweepstake on the same Doncaster Cup day, he never won again in thirteen outings. As a five year old he was unplaced in both the Royal Hunt Cup and in the Stewards' Cup at Goodwood, where he started at odds of 50/1 giving the winner three stone four pounds. This was his final race. He went to stud at Blankney for the modest fee of twenty guineas. His success surpassed all anticipation. He was Leading Sire seven consecutive years from 1880 to 1886. He sired the winners of seven Classic races: Thebais (1881 One Thousand Guineas and Oaks), St Marguerite (1882 One Thousand Guineas), Shotiver (1882 Two Thousand Guineas and Derby), St Blaise (1883 Derby) and Lonely (1885 Oaks). He also sired Tristan, winner of the July Cup, the Epsom Gold Cup (now the Coronation Cup) twice, the Hardwicke Stakes three times, the Ascot Gold Cup, and the Champion Stakes three times. All but Lonely were chesnuts. Hermit's fee rose to three hundred guineas, although five hundred guineas was paid on some occasions. Hermit lived to the age of twenty-six and died on 29 April 1890. In all, his progeny won 846 races.

Henry Chaplin, meanwhile, devoted much of his time to politics. A typical Tory squire, he rose to the position of Minister of Agriculture and was raised to the peerage in 1916. He died in 1923; even into his eighties he openly admitted Hermit was the best friend he ever had.

A Day Out with Winlaw

TIM HEALD

I have been trying to go racing with Winlaw for years.

Winlaw is a National Hunt handicapper but I first met him in the Parks at Oxford watching cricket on a desolate April day when the University were playing Hampshire. We were in the hospitality tent provided by a man called Ted Tichbon, who ran the Oxford Travel Agency, and we were sheltering from the cold. Winlaw's full name is A.S.R. de W. Winlaw and some people call him Tony. When his birth was announced in *The Times* the 'R' came before the 'S', but luckily this was spotted before the christening and the batting order was reversed, otherwise he would have been forever 'ARSE' Winlaw. In any case his wife and other intimates call him Winlaw and so do I. This first meeting was in 1985 and there was something about the man, old-fashioned and old Harrovian, which demanded that I should call him simply by his surname. Winlaw. A good name. It belongs in a novel.

Winlaw's father was a gilded tragedy, a double Cambridge blue killed in World War Two when his Spitfire collided with another somewhere over Wales. Winlaw himself became a useful cricketer, though never as good as his father. After school at Harrow he was apprenticed at the *Daily Telegraph* under E.W. (Jim) Swanton as a writer. A knowledgeable punter, he was then, some twenty years ago, offered a job handicapping horses and decided to leave the *Telegraph* and freelance, combining the handicapping with a spot of cricket writing.

In those days both were occupations for what one might laughingly describe as 'gentlemen'. In other words they didn't involve a lot of work and they did involve a lot of 'socializing'. 'Socializing' is a euphemism for hanging around in bars.

Times have changed. In 1994 Winlaw was no longer writing

about cricket. And whereas he had once been an intuitive and inspired member of a team of thirteen handicappers, he was now one of only three survivors who appeared to do most of their work, prosaically, on computers. Demonstrably and indisputably Winlaw is a gent, but like a lot of gents these days he often seems marginally distressed as if left over from some previous and now-discredited regime.

I liked Winlaw from the first, not least because he seemed out of time, a man swimming breast-stroke against the tide of history. He belongs to White's Club in St James's. Later, when I got to know him properly – though improperly is a more apt adverb when it comes to Winlaw – we had a memorable lunch with Sir William Becher, Bt, the charming but stupendously deaf secretary of the I Zingari cricket club. How Winlaw shouted! It was there too that Winlaw bought me a bullshot, a mixture of vodka, Campbell's (it simply must be Campbell's) bouillon, Worcester sauce, lemon juice, celery salt and various other semi-mysterious ingredients.

He had made a jug of something similar the night before the day we finally did go racing together. It was in the study of his house in Shipston-on-Stour, Warwickshire. We had tried seriously to come under starter's orders thrice previously. Warwick, Towcester and Warwick again had all fallen foul of the weather. The last attempt had been peculiarly depressing. Winlaw had assured me that racing would take place come hell, high water or heavy frost. I stayed the night at the Traveller's, took an early train and a taxi from the station only to find the racecourse hoar-white and padlocked. Curses, curses. The station buffet in Leamington Spa is no place to spend a snowy February afternoon.

Our fourth and final attempt was Chepstow, just over the Severn Bridge. I took the 5.10 from Paddington, wearing a suit and my Herbert Johnson hat, was met by Winlaw and chauffeured to a home full of cricket paintings and horsy rosettes. Winlaw's wife cooked a memorable kitchen supper and we drank the bullshot, claret and port. His sister-in-law was over from Naas in County Kildare where her husband trains. He was once Irish champion jockey but fell into bad odour when, in the sixties, he pulled up the favourite in horribly heavy going at the Cheltenham Gold Cup. After dinner Winlaw entertained me with readings from the *Harrow School Register*.

Next day we paused briefly in Moreton-in-Marsh, where Winlaw exchanged an ill-considered purchase – a vivid blue suit – at the Sue Ryder shop, and we swung north. At this point Winlaw inserted a tape of Harrow School songs of the sort which once reduced Winston Churchill to tears. All the way to Chepstow we listened to the massed male voices singing in a mixture of English and dog-Latin about the pleasures of nude bathing, rugby football, the old school and all that. From time to time Winlaw joined in, more or less word perfect, until, an hour or so later, we crossed the Severn into Wales, stuck an official red sticker on the windscreen and motored majestically through the stone gateposts of the race-course to the strains of 'Forty Years On' accompanied by Winlaw, fortissimo.

The main stand at Chepstow has a definite sense of Croydon aerodrome, *circa* 1930. It is a large white edifice with glass excrescences like control towers tacked on top as afterthoughts – not a thing of beauty, though the course itself is charming, an undulating oval with the cliffs along the Wye in the background and soft Hereford hills beyond.

Winlaw went off to sort out passes and touch base leaving me alone for a moment or two. I remembered the only other time I had been to the races here, more than a decade ago, when my wife and I had been at a weekend wine-tasting and slept in a bed like a wrought-iron hammock. It snowed in the night and we drove past Tintern Abbey shrouded in Christmas-card-white woods to the racing, which was cold beyond belief but also pretty.

I could never describe myself as a racing man, I thought, despite my hat, brown and wide brimmed and more of a racing hat than some of the pork-pie jobs coming through the turnstiles as I waited for Winlaw's return. Nevertheless racing had punctuated my life from time to time and there was something about it which was enormously appealing and escapist. For me, a day at the races is always 'a willing suspension of disbelief'.

The elderly figure of Peter O'Sullevan entered left. I remembered him from my days on the *Daily Express*. He and the late Clive Graham, a.k.a. 'The Scout', once took me to Sandown Park for a day with the bookie Victor Chandler. I seem to recollect a lot of brandy and ginger ale.

Sandown was my most regular track. Years ago my father worked for W.D. and H.O. Wills, the tobacco people. They sponsored races and sometimes my mother was called upon to present a cup. My father was also, improbably, a member of the Variety Club of Great Britain and every year the Club sponsored a Sandown meeting. It was full of big hats and cleavage and half-forgotten movie moguls like Nat Cohen of Hammer Films with his dapper moustache. I once went to Cohen's house and was amazed and rather shocked when he used Dom Perignon for making champagne cocktails. One year I took my friend Angela to the Variety Club meeting and we had lunch at Wheeler's before taking the train from Waterloo and walking across the course from the funny little railway station, on stilts and more like a remote mid-Welsh halt than suburban Surrey. And there was that time in the pouring rain when racing was resumed after some industrial dispute. A jockeys' strike? Was that possible? All the national papers sent their sketch writers down to cover the first day back and we were practically the only people there. Norman Shrapnel came from the *Guardian* and Philip Howard from *The Times*. We all got wet.

I was musing on this when Winlaw returned with a blue member's pass which he tried rather ineffectually to loop through the lapel of my riding mac. A dapper Julian Wilson trotted past in regulation hat, regulation brown coat and tweeds with obligatory binoculars. Wilson works for the BBC, and the BBC were televising the first few races. Wilson is the son of Peter Wilson, once, famously, the chief sports writer on the *Daily Mirror*. He was described by them as 'the Man they can't gag' and he was my godfather. Larger than life was the usual phrase for describing Peter – his son, I think, less so.

Winlaw said that we were to lunch with the other officials: the vet, the starter, the clerk to the stewards and so on. We found them in the members' restaurant, all tweed and outdoor complexion. The restaurant was like racecourse restaurants everywhere – straightforward, old-fashioned food, rather over-priced. The clientele was also familiar. Such places always seem to contain women of a certain age in fur and too much makeup with men in velvet collared overcoats sucking on cigars, not always lit. The atmosphere is appealingly louche. I always feel that, if not exactly villainous, most lunchers in racecourse restaurants are not up to a lot of good.

The first race was at 1 p.m. It was called the Hywel Davies

Retirement Hurdle over 'Two Miles About Half a Furlong'. I like
the inexactitude. There were only four runners. Generally speaking
the fields that afternoon were all small. This was partly because the
following week was Cheltenham, partly because the going was
heavy. There were other reasons too, according to Winlaw, but
they were too abstruse to follow.

I watched the first race from a private box occupied by the owner
of a grand hotel in Llandrindrod Wells. Winlaw was wearing a
garish striped tie, which indicated that he was a member of the
South Wales Hunt cricket club. The hotel owner was wearing the
same tie. He was a jovial cove who had also been at school at
Harrow. Winlaw told him he had been singing the old songs in
the car and his eyes lit up. Like several of the more prosperous
racegoers, he had grown a little too stout for his suit. He plied
me with wine and made banteringly disparaging remarks about
Winlaw.

I have to concede that I'm not altogether clear exactly what
Winlaw did or was supposed to do that afternoon. He watched
every race from a glass control-tower-style box at the top of the
unsaddling enclosure in the company of the stewards. It seemed to
me that his presence there was a sort of 'just in case' job. In the
event of something untoward happening Winlaw might be called
upon to intervene. But if everything went according to plan all he
had to do was ease around. Most of his real work seemed to take
place at home with the computer.

What was immediately apparent was that he knew most of the
people on the course. After lunch he decided a cigar was called for.
Going to a mobile tobacco and confectionery kiosk he purchased
a large Havana but decided it was over-priced and tried to beat
the price down. Eventually and with some reluctance the vendor
knocked off 25p. A little later I bought myself a very much cheaper
cigar. 'I've known your friend getting on twenty years,' said the
cigar seller, 'and every time he argues about the price.' He said this
with a wry smile and some affection.

There was also the matter of snuff. The night before, Winlaw
had given me snuff, the first time I had tried any for more than a
quarter of a century. I had always thought that the correct way of
taking the stuff was to apply a little to the back of one's hand and
snort it, but apparently this is incorrect. The right way is to take

a pinch and use two fingers to insert it up the nostril. Not elegant but apparently less explosive.

Chepstow that day was rife with snuff-taking. The chief dispenser was a wild-eyed snuff baron with white mutton-chop whiskers, who mixed his own and, according to Winlaw, has a fine cellar of snuff at his home in Llanvihangel Gobion near Abergavenny. The *on dit* at Chepstow was that one simply never bought shop snuff. You mixed your own. Winlaw and I cadged mercilessly and later ran into another man with a box of home-mix, which Winlaw pronounced even better than the snuff from Llanvihangel Gobion. It was quite strange though. I have seldom seen so many middle-aged or elderly men with fingers stuck up their noses.

The second race was the Bishop Memorial, a novices' handicap named after a racegoing cleric called the Rev James Fisher, who was very tall and had attended this very meeting the previous year only to collapse and die immediately afterwards. Chepstow was his favourite course and so his friends had clubbed together and put up the money for a race in his memory. He was never a bishop but that was his nickname. I thought this rather charming and typical, somehow, of racing. Every course should contain at least one gambling clergyman.

The next race, the 2 p.m., was the big race, The Beaufort Hurdle with £17,500 added. This was won by Relkeel, so-named because the parents were Relkino and Secret Keel. (There is an interesting treatise to be written about the naming of racehorses.) Winlaw was especially pleased about this because Relkeel's owner, present in a wheelchair but able to stand for the presentation of the trophy, was the 93-year-old Brigadier 'Roscoe' Harvey. The Brigadier was the Senior Stewards' Secretary of the Jockey Club from 1951 to 1968 and Winlaw rated him very highly. Indeed he described him as 'the most respected of all officials in our lifetime'. The presentation was made by Colonel Harry Llewellyn, father of Dai and Roddy, and the winner, on Foxhunter, of Britain's only gold medal in the Helsinki Olympics. The horse was ridden by the season's most successful jockey, Adrian Maguire, a fresh-faced gnome who impressed everyone by helicoptering off in the middle of the afternoon to ride in some races at Sandown.

For once I didn't bet, not even with Mick Fletcher ('Cash Taken'), who was intriguingly described as 'The Asparagus Kid'. I was experiencing a temporary – I hoped – cash-flow problem at the time. Besides I was having too much fun hanging around the private boxes with the jolly hotel owner, the mutton-chopped snuff baron and their friends. Another unexpected host was a Colin Davies, who trained the great Champion Hurdler, Persian War, who won the title at Cheltenham with a hat-trick in 1968, 1969 and 1970. Persian War has a bar named after him at Chepstow and Winlaw says he was probably the best ever. Another of Mr Davies's claims to fame is that his daughter married Philip Blacker, riding, sculpting son of the legendary General Sir Cecil 'Monkey' Blacker. He was preening himself because his son-in-law had just been elected to the Jockey Club.

Winlaw had promised that he would introduce me to the course Chairman, G.H.C. Clay, son of the greatest of all Welsh cricketers, J.C. Clay, but Winlaw had very little luck with Clay, a lofty figure seemingly always on the move. Every time Winlaw approached him he was waved away with a dismissive 'Not now, later.' Because he is a paid official Winlaw gets a certain amount of this from some stewards and their kind. It's one reason, that, unlike other handicappers, he never goes into the Paddock along with the stewards, owners and trainers. At one of his very first meetings he was rudely snubbed by some steward whom Winlaw regarded as very much his inferior. He has harboured a bit of a grudge ever since. The other class of person he doesn't much care for is the sort of trainer who berates him for handicapping one of his horses too severely. In the old days he says that would never have happened but nowadays one or two chaps who should know better have jolly bad manners.

There were only three horses in the Llangibby Handicap and six in the Curre Handicap. To be honest I don't think the racing was very spectacular but as usual for me that wasn't the point of the exercise.

All my life a day at the races has been a day out of time in which the actual racing has been necessary but only incidental. I remember picnics at Kempton and Veuve Clicquot champagne in a tent on a sunny day at Salisbury. I remember a keening wind on a bleak day at Wincanton; oh, and elegant high-stepping horses pulling little chariots round a snowy course in Toronto and feisty little quarter-horses on a dirt track in Santa Fe, New Mexico, and much else besides – smells and sights and always that slight sense of mischief and escape and people who are less than good.

And now to that rag-bag of recollection I can add my day at Chepstow with Winlaw. As he said in a subsequent note, 'I think at least there was some Character about Chepstow.' As we walked back to the car I thought of men too big for their suits, and the sharing of snuff and the haggling over a Havana. When Winlaw turned on the ignition Harrow School were still singing 'Forty Years On'. Then, moments later, they slid into 'Auld Lang Syne'.

We struck out south towards the Severn and Winlaw joined in, almost word perfect as before.

I had been trying to go racing with him for years, and now, finally, I had managed it, and was pleased.

A Season's Dreamin'

GEE ARMYTAGE

It's just turned August. The new National Hunt season has started and I haven't sat on a horse since 6 June.

My trip to Australia with Lorna Vincent to ride against girls from New Zealand, the USA and of course the Aussies was supposed to have been a summer break. A break it was for me – of my left elbow in two places, kicked by a horse we were standing next to out hunting, on our third day there. I don't believe it – a chance to represent my country and get to see the world for free and it's off to hospital after one race in our fourteen-day programme. Hunting is a pastime I no longer cherish as I would have done as a child fifteen years ago; but then a lot has happened since then.

A rise to the big time – good press, winners, more press, more winners, magazines, TV shows and Lady Riders' Championships; fun, humour and great nights out – life on the edge.

It's now two months since I've ridden and it's been two months of thinking, hoping, worrying, speculating and indeed praying. What really lies ahead? I'm still madly in love with the racing game but it rarely shows me much affection nowadays.

The high point and the low point of last season was the Stakis Scottish Grand National. The joy, the pain and a haunting question. Why, in the dying strides of a great race when I needed a last smooth take-off and landing as badly as I had ever needed anything, did it not happen? Had I gone for a long one would Merry Master have come up for me or gone down? It is a question that must remain unanswered. As it was we got in too close, lost impulsion and Run For Free and Mark Perrett got up to beat us by a neck. My feelings were torn. I had had a great ride and come so close; but sometimes the closer you get the more painful it is.

The race had a special meaning because I was riding for my

father and the win would have meant so much to the yard. Dad had saddled Barona to win two consecutive Scottish Nationals in the 1970s, long before I took up the reins of anything larger than my first pony.

But that was yesterday and is consigned to memory. Today is the time for looking forward. I have been to see the specialist about my elbow and the X-rays showed a minute improvement but overall the break has not consolidated yet. I am given three choices by Mr Foy. A bone graft, a pin to replace the wires which are currently holding it together or to press on slowly. The first two options will set me back to day one so the decision makes itself. Basically the wires will hold the arm in place so barring a fall all should be well and I can start rebuilding some muscle. Realistically my chances of getting back on the track before October are slim.

I start running again and working on the good parts. I am amazed at how quickly I lose condition – no wonder some horses take what seems for ever to come back from an enforced lay off. But at least I don't have to explain it to an owner.

Good news and not bad timing. I can start riding out for Simon Sherwood in two weeks' time. I have been hoping to ride out for Simon for some time as he trains within walking distance, but he has not really required me before, besides which in previous seasons I have been too busy dashing all over the place riding and schooling for various trainers in the hope of picking up a spare race ride. Competition for rides has never been more fierce and I am hardly in fashion just at the moment, but it is amazing what a few winners would do.

It's dangerous to bank all on one race but just now I haven't too many options. April and the Grand National are a long way off and there are many questions to be answered before then. Will my intended mount, Merry Master, be fit? Will he stay uninjured this season? Will I be able to stay out of the wars? Many people are doing much to help me realize my dream. My father has delayed his retirement to train Merry Master for one more year and, most importantly, Geoff Lansbury, the owner of the horse, has stayed loyal to me. I feel a great sense of responsibility to them.

I hear that Rosemary Henderson may ride Fiddlers Pike at Aintree, but I doubt if there will be any other of the fairer sex competing. The race has changed now that the top weight has come down to eleven stone ten pounds. The bottom weights are not getting as much of an advantage as they were when certain horses were set to carry twelve stone and more. With the fence alterations of recent years having made jumping easier, the race is liable to be won by one of the more fancied runners. I have no doubt the season will throw up some extra special long-distance horses as always.

Eighteenth of September, my first ride back and it's a winner. Romola Nijinsky trained by Mr Evans comfortably won the Ladies Handicap Hurdle at Stratford. Michael Turner the racecourse doctor advised me against riding but said that since it was not life-threatening he would leave the decision to me. Tomorrow I'm having the wires removed from my arm. The little horse had a good chance of winning, so I took it and it paid off.

My fitness is improving daily and now the arm is free to mend on its own, I feel good. Merry Master is about a month away from his first race of the season, which is planned for Wetherby in late October. We are beginning to think he may like good to firm ground in his later years. Some horses do change their preference as they get older but the season seems to be a particularly wet one so far.

A phone call from one of the Sunday journalists and I find that I am repeating myself. 'I'm hooked on racing and the adrenaline flows, although hovering between a feeling of great expectation and bitter disappointment.' It must be true because I do believe it. I refuse to answer the second question which is all about listing injuries. I suppose it is human nature but I do find it monotonous. The press has been more than kind to me over the years so I try to be helpful. One day the phone will stop ringing.

Merry Master ran well on our comeback trail today, finishing second to Mr Boston at Wetherby.

All the early signs are that 'The Master' has summered well and we may have reason to be optimistic about the Hennessy at Newbury next month. Plans will have to be made if we decide to run him in it. He is a natural front runner but it will be playing into our opponents' hands unless we can steal a big lead and hope to hang on. This race is often a good guide to the National and its results will have the pundits of form sifting through it again and again.

The Hennessy has come and gone and the sooner the better. We employed the front-running tactics and it proved to be our downfall. We led into the final straight and were swallowed up by the field in a matter of one fence, finishing sixth. I am not very happy about it but then we knew the risks we were running. We simply got it wrong.

It all seems so important nowadays and it is. Unlike the days of 1987 and 1988 when everything seemed so carefree. Even the day at Leicester, brother Marcus, Martin Bosley, Richard Dunwoody and I set off in a novice chase along with fourteen others and I see from the records that Marcus was behind when he tried to refuse and was unseated. Martin was behind from the 8th and fell at the 13th. Richard blundered and was unseated at the 10th and I made a mistake at the 7th, weakened at the 12th and fell at the 14th. We all hitched a ride back in the ambulance together. I was just pleased to have got the farthest. What a crazy sport this is!

It might have all been different if I hadn't got hooked by having my first winner. I am thankful I never took drugs: I would have been a certainty to become an addict. I had intended to make a career out of show jumping like my mother, who represented Great Britain for a number of years in the late fifties and early sixties, but the buzz is greater when riding at speed. My great friend Tina Cassan, with whom I went to school, has gone on to become one of the leading lights in the show-jumping world. As kids she and I had a couple of really good ponies and although I hate to admit it we were a menace when out hunting.

Twenty-eighth of December, the Welsh National. Yet another disappointment. Merry Master was never going well and he fell when going out on the second circuit. I wonder if he has a bug of some sort. He never took hold of the bridle in his normal way and he was beaten when he fell at half way – not like him. Perhaps this is another race best forgotten – but it is not helping to keep my dream alive. It is also not helping to pay his way.

Thirteenth of January, Wetherby and again second. That's better. He was shouldering a lot of weight and this was not a bad performance. Particularly in ground we believe he no longer likes. He is running in and out of form this season – not at all like last year when he ran up a sequence of wins.

His jumping used to give cause for concern but I like to think age and experience have helped him to look after us both and we seem to have reached an understanding. Aintree is different and you cannot treat those fences with anything but respect. Certain horses will love the course and others will hate it. Gee A, who gave me a real thrill around here, started off by being a terrible jumper. I had been advised by any number of professional jockeys not to ride him and he fell on the first two occasions we came together. Later on he made a name for both of us at Cheltenham and Liverpool. I do believe it was all down to confidence with him.

He was my first ride for Geoff Hubbard – and what a wonderful owner *he* became to me. He really got me going and gave me plenty of rides early on in my career. His horses were trained by Ferdy Murphy at Woodbridge in Suffolk, a county I know best in the early hours of dawn, when I used to drive there from Newbury, often leaving at 4 a.m.

I must admit to having been up in front of the stewards on more than one occasion for excessive use of the whip. This was early on and I have learnt to curb my enthusiasm by now. The subject of whip abuse will not lie down and it causes many feelings of injustice within the weighing room. Too many people are expected to pass opinions on what is excessive and what is not and each one has a different idea. The Jockeys' Association and Portman Square are at odds over the interpretation of the rules but at least the efforts that are being made should produce results eventually.

Twenty-sixth of February, the Greenall Whitney Gold Cup was to have been run at Haydock but the weather has been so appalling that it has moved to Kempton. The dream is still alive! We ran third to Master Oates, only beaten one length by Moorcroft Boy for second place, and these two are being spoken of as likely favourites for 9 April at Liverpool. Merry Master ran a really brave and honest race – what a hero he is when he goes like this. Dad has a real knack of having his horses ready for the big races and I am sure he won't let us down on the day.

The Cheltenham Festival comes first and I am very honoured to have been asked to open 'Gee's Marquee', an idea of Edward Gillespie, the Managing Director of The Racecourse Company. It is hoped it will become a haven for younger members to meet, eat and drink. It is on trial this year but is hoped to become a permanent feature.

The Festival was a brilliant three days with some really magic winners. Who would have thought that France would provide us with the Gold Cup winner after so many gallant failures? Two short heads should have been enough to see off the invader once and for all but it was a magnificent effort and The Fellow has written himself his own special page of history.

Flakey Dove's Champion Hurdle was a wonderful happening for the small stable of Richard Price, whose family had bred not only her but also her forebears. There are just two for whom the dreams have come true.

The Midlands Grand National took place today, Saturday, 19 March and all is gloom again. Merry Master bowled along in front for two of the three circuits and I was forced to pull up half way through the third. Yes, it must be the ground but what if it is? Will this rain never cease? If it goes on like it has been, is there any point in running at Aintree? Are we better to save him for another crack at the Scottish? Will I have to awake from my dream?

Postscript

Oh, well. As things turned out, I wasn't to realize my dream after all – not this season, anyway. A few days before the National I was in bed with a temperature of a hundred and I don't know what, but still hoping to ride. On the day, the temperature had subsided . . .

. . . and so had the ground, battered into submission by torrential rain until it had gone from a reasonable good-to-firm a week before the race to an impossible soggy-going-on-quicksand on the day. We withdrew, and I was left hoping for consolation in the Scottish National a few days afterwards.

I came fifth, which, in the context – twenty-three runners, less than ideal going even then, residual snuffles and a modest dose of depression thrown in for bad measure – wasn't all that bad. I couldn't help thinking, though: if only it had been fifth in the Big One, how much better that would have been . . .

. . . but the thing about dreams is that, if you've only got the strength to keep them in proportion, know them for what they are, well, there's always another season, another good horse. Another dream. Watch this space . . .

'Tall Oaks from Little Acorns Grow'

IAN WALLACE

Yes, my love affair with horseracing was as slow to burgeon as an oak from an acorn. When I was seven or eight in the 1920s, we had a cat called Tishy named after a famous racehorse who appeared to cross his front legs while galloping. Our cat only crossed his front legs when he was sitting down, but there you are.

One day my father, a Scots presbyterian with a twinkle in his eye, called out to me, 'Come on, Steve!' I was lagging behind on a walk. When I mutinously protested that Steve wasn't my name, he told me the crowd used to shout it to a famous jockey called Steve Donoghue as he urged his winners up the final straight. Odd really because, so far as I know, my father never attended a race meeting in his life.

During the war I spent nearly two years in a hospital near Epsom lying in a plaster cast with a spinal complaint. Whether it was the proximity of one of the most famous racecourses in the world or the fact that one of our hospital porters was a retired jockey it's impossible to say, but on Saturdays when there were race meetings, gambling fever gripped our ward.

George, a fellow patient with a shock of bristly ginger hair and a moustache to match who was recovering from hair-raising injuries sustained on a motor bike, was the instigator. He was the sort of man who would bet on two drips of water on a window, and he had 'connections', he told us, who supplied him with 'information'.

'You want to get your money on Way In ante post for the Guineas,' he told me. 'You can get tens now and he'll cake-walk it. Probably start odds on. This friend of mine had it straight from the head lad.'

I didn't know what he was talking about and at twenty-three too ashamed to admit my ignorance. When he'd gone I asked Moses,

Mo for short, our former jockey turned porter, who enlightened me and advised against this particular flutter. *His* 'connections' told a different story. In the event both were wrong.

But on Saturdays, coached by George on the intricacies of accumulator bets, most of us had small but complicated wagers which, in the wildly unlikely event of our three or even four fancied horses coming up roses in different races on the same afternoon, stood to win us £5 or even £10 for an initial stake of half a crown. The trouble was that if the first two won you couldn't change your mind and withdraw with your winnings before they went on number three. A winning treble or quadruple was about as likely as a football pool jackpot. We knew nothing about horses or the comfortable life style of the bookmakers that depended on suckers like us. We couldn't have cared less. It was worth half a crown to relieve the monotony.

Off-course betting was illegal in those days and betting in the hospital was forbidden, but Mo knew a bookie who would gladly accept our hopeful offerings.

We wrote down the bets on slips of paper and gave them to Mo plus the money. 'If I'm caught with this lot,' he used to say every week, 'I'll be sacked on the spot. They might search me at the gate but I'm up to that, I put the slips in me hat.' What would have happened if a funeral had gone past or he'd met the matron didn't bear thinking about. The diminutive Mo with his bandy legs and white hair carefully brushed into a quiff was not one of nature's optimists. I can still see him in his brown alpaca coat strewing the ward floor with tea leaves and often, as he was sweeping them up near my spinal carriage, he would lean on his broom and say, 'When are they going to get you up, sir? I've heard you'll never walk again.' A barrel of laughs was Mo.

One Friday evening Neil, a young fair-haired Scots lieutenant whom I'd known slightly before the war, handed me a slip of paper and half a crown. 'I've got a weekend pass. Be a good chap and give this to Mo tomorrow. He might forget it if I give it him today.'

Next morning I looked at the racing page of my paper and decided that nothing appealed to me. I glanced at Neil's treble that he'd given me the previous evening. The first bet was a longish shot followed by two very short-priced favourites. I decided to give the horses a miss that week and settled down to an Agatha Christie.

It was with horror I realized at teatime I'd forgotten to give Mo Neil's bet. Mo wouldn't be in till Sunday morning, there was no way of getting an evening paper and in those days the wireless didn't give racing results. I consoled myself through Saturday evening with the thought that Neil would be delighted to get his half crown back when he returned on Sunday evening. One of his nags was bound to have bitten the dust. Wasn't it?

You're ahead of me. After the *Sunday Express* fell from my nerveless fingers I spent a short while with pencil and paper working out what I owed him. It was something in the region of £8. 5s. 0d. In 1943 a second lieutenant's pay was 11s. a day, so it was nearly two weeks' wages.

Fortunately my generous and concerned parents saw to it that I had money on hand for books, cigarettes, beer etc. so when Neil, tall and debonair, came striding into the ward with a great big grin on his face, I was able to pay him out (just) and get the word 'congratulations' over my larynx. 'Don't forget to tip Mo,' I said. Mo was my only confidant in this sorry affair. 'Tell the bugger you forgot' had been his robustly sensible advice. Unfortunately the genes from my presbyterian father made that an impossible option.

A week or two later George hobbled over to my carriage brandishing a letter. 'Listen,' he said, 'I've got this friend who runs an unlicensed dog track outside Nottingham. He's written to say there's a wonderful bitch running there on Saturday, nobody knows how good she is and she'll start at 7/1. I'm going up there, so if you give me a couple of quid . . .' but I'd had enough.

Nothing in all this to explain my present emotional love of racing and Newmarket racecourse in particular, though I moved a step nearer when the Derby that year (1943) was won by an Epsom-trained horse called Straight Deal and we were all on him. Mo staggered into the ward clinking like a gaoler's key-ring. He'd been paid out for all of us in silver – the bookie's revenge.

Things moved a little faster two or three years later when I was lucky enough to have made a sufficiently good recovery to embark on an operatic career. The Italian conductor of the first opera company I sang in recommended me to have lessons with a Neapolitan singing teacher called Rodolfo Mele, a brilliant and lovable teddy bear of a man, who lived with his Scots wife in Holland Park in west London, which saved me from having to go to Italy for advanced training.

I had been a pupil for a year or so and we had become friends before he let me into his secret. He was a very successful punter, and the element of luck in his bets was reduced to a minimum by hard work with the form book and his own records, which he began to update as soon as his last pupil for the day had gone.

'Ian,' he told me all of forty years ago, 'I know a little about racing. My uncle trained trotters in Italy when I was a boy and I learn a lot from 'eem. I give every horse points for all kinds of things. When they win I look up the time in the form book. I can compare that time witha the same time on other courses. I know alla the courses. Some have a right hand curve, some a left, some 'ave 'ills, some are level. Some horses go better left than right, and I knowa which they are. Then there are the weights, and the skill of the jockeys. You have to consider every horse in the race and see which has most points. Issa hard work but it pays off. Issa maddening when two horses ina the same race 'ave equal points.'

He handed me a large notebook with pages of columns and figures opposite the names of horses. It was clearly a mathematical exercise of great complexity. I handed it back shaking my head in wonder.

'I tell you something,' he went on. 'Beforea the War one daily newspaper offer me £10,000 a year to be their tipster. Everyone knew I had many winners and so they come for me. I say no thank you very much, I'm a singing teacher who goes racing now and then, not a professional punter.' He smiled and chuckled at the memory of it.

'Then a bookie comea to me and say, "I gotta proposition. You are very clever at knowing who wins, so I tell you whatta we'll do. When every horse is tryin', you tell us who'sa going to win. When they're not all tryin', we'll tell you." I turn 'eem down too. Thatta way you end up down on the rails with a knife in your back.'

I became more and more intrigued by Rodolfo's stories of his forays to race meetings. Usually on Saturdays, though he'd shut his studio for a big mid-week race, always by train, he would go as far as Doncaster or Chepstow, always betting with bookies rather than the Tote. 'I likea to see the money come out of the satchel and the look on their face.'

He told me how several bookies wouldn't bet with him because he won too often, and there were the heart-rending stories of the ones that got away. 'The number of times I lose by a short 'ead's amazin'.'

One summer in the 1950s, after my lesson, he said, 'Ian, let'sa go racin' together. There's a meetin' at Goodwood whilea you're at Glyndebourne. We go a day you're notta singin'.'

What a beautiful setting for a racecourse! Perched high on the Sussex Downs with green rolling countryside stretching away wherever you look – a spectacular panorama, particularly on a sparkling July day, and it was clear that the crowd, ranging from high fashion to low scruff, were enjoying not only the races but a day in the country as well. A seagull riding the thermals over the grandstand gave a cheerful reminder that the sea is only a dozen miles away.

'We pay to be day members, Ian, issa not cheap, but we can seea the horses in the Paddock beforea the race and check 'ow they look.' He studied his race-card. 'Scobie Breasley issa riding five cats, we don'ta back any of them.'

Mr Breasley was a famous Australian jockey nearing the end of his long career in England where he was highly popular, and at this stage in his career was affectionately known to the punters as 'grandad'. Well, 'grandad' did them proud. Despite Rodolfo's disparaging comments about each of the 'cats' as they minced their way round the Paddock before the race with their lads straining at the bridle, a smiling Breasley cantered them up to the start and brought all five in first. The crowd went mad – except for us.

Poor Rodolfo. He'd wanted to show me his forecasting at its best and had picked probably his only disastrous meeting of the year to try to impress me.

'Come on, Ian, I've 'ad enough, letsa go home.'

'No', I said, 'there's one more race, surely you can pick one winner today. I want to get back all that entrance money you made me pay.' It was unfair and I knew it. I hadn't lost much money on the betting. Notes stick to my wallet like flypaper on a racecourse, and I was only a few pounds down, but I felt that all 'grandad's' supporters had taken the bookies to the cleaners and I'd been warned off putting a penny on him all afternoon.

'All right, Ian,' said Rodolfo. 'You stay here. I go and see someone.' I watched him go through the barrier into the public enclosure and head for a man standing down by the rails. He was unshaven, his dark grey suit down at heel and his half-smoked rolled cigarette was stuck to his lower lip, jerking up and down when he spoke. He wore a battered homburg pulled well down over his face. He shook hands with Rodolfo somewhat reluctantly and after an earnest conversation, Rodolfo handed him a pound note, patted him on the shoulder and returned to me in triumph. 'Puta alla you can afford on number six, Ian. 'E'll win.' I thought of George in the hospital and his 'information'.

Nevertheless, I plunged. At least £3. What followed was completely unexpected. From the stand we could see the start and number six, a lively chesnut colt, was giving a fair imitation of a bucking bronco at a rodeo. He kept kicking out with both hind legs and no handlers or other horses dared go near. His jockey, whose name I forget, was miraculously adhesive, and when it seemed that the others might be started without number six, he ran away with the jockey and completed the whole seven furlongs at a cracking pace and was only pulled up hundreds of yards farther on.

The jockey turned him round and trotted him demurely back past the stands to the start.

'That's torn it,' I said. 'He'll never have the strength to do it again.'

''E'll win,' was Rodolfo's laconic response, and he did, easily. I recovered my entrance money and there wasn't even a stewards' inquiry.

'Who was that man?'

Rodolfo shrugged his shoulders. 'Issa just someone who know a thing or two.'

With which I had to be content. We never went racing again, but he was my friend and mentor till he died and I still miss him.

None of this explains why now in old age I often turn to the racing page of the paper before the cricket or football (all of them read before steeling myself for page one), or why I now watch racing on TV with avid interest and go with my wife to Newmarket when we can. It's simple really. Let me explain.

In 1954 we went on a spring holiday to Tossa de Mar. There were no huge hotels then, no tourists, no noise except for the jingle of a donkey's harness and the frogs croaking near the water. In the modest hotel was an English honeymoon couple, whom we studiously avoided until one day they suggested we joined them for coffee after lunch. Within a day or two we knew, and it's a rare experience, that they would be friends for life. He was a young veterinary surgeon about to join a practice in Newmarket.

He and I were immersed in our careers and hardly met for thirty years but never lost touch. He has become one of the most distinguished equine veterinary surgeons in the world, and his wife, more as a hobby than anything else, has made a great name as what the racing fraternity describe as a small breeder. Two mares shrewdly covered have delivered some excellent results in recent years.

When I became semi-retired, these two dear souls began inviting us to Newmarket races or 'just to see the foals if you're passing', and we often pass on our way to our Norfolk cottage. Soon I realized that their great love of horses and the people who ride and look after them was infectious, and that horseracing for me was nothing to do with 'information' or backing 'a lot of cats'. It was nothing to do with betting at all. It was an emotional feeling about these marvellous animals and the brightly dressed gnomes who get on their backs, about the atmosphere of the racecourse, the dramatic sequence from paddock to start, to winning or losing, about walking round a top trainer's yard and giving Polo mints to a yearling that just might win a classic race one day.

Soon our friends, whose names I won't mention though anyone in racing will have identified them from the clues already given, introduced us to the Yearling Sales at Tattersalls, which for me is pure theatre, as the spirited youngsters and their handlers go endlessly round the ring and inscrutable bidders in the steeply raked circular auditorium make tiny movements of hand or programme and the sellers sit impassive and stressed like football managers in the last five minutes. We've stood beside them near the winning post at Newmarket and shared the tremendous thrill and euphoria of seeing one of that 'small breeder's' two year olds winning the Middle Park Stakes, and then gone on to watch one of his yearling relations bring up six figures on the electric price indicator in Tattersalls a few hours later.

Yes, they have to sell the foals they breed, but the prices get higher and we all watch their progress on the racecourse with a mixture of affection, enthusiasm and excitement. Thanks to them my acorn has at last become a tree.

The Rise and Rise of My Uncle Ernie

DAVID BENEDICTUS

Don't Boast About It – Market It

Do you know what an A-Board is? I bought one in East Sheen. An A-Board is the sort of thing you see on the pavement with 'Today's Special: Steak and Kidney Pie £2.75' chalked on it. It is called an A-Board because the shape of the thing, two slats hinged at the top and linked halfway down by chains or straps, calls the letter A inevitably to mind. On the A-Board I bought in East Sheen I wrote (in coloured tape – chalk would not have been prominent enough):

'WIN! WIN! WIN! WITH UNCLE ERNIE!'

and on the reverse, impressive claims detailing just how much you would have won won won if you had been fortunate enough to have followed Uncle Ernie's advice during the previous Flat Season.

Uncle Ernie seemed the right name for The System. We considered Uncle Harry, but that sounded flash. We considered Uncle Jack, after my real and subversive maternal uncle, but Ernie hinted strongly at earnings, which was good, and Ernie, the computer which chooses the random Premium Bond winners, which was better. We settled for Uncle Ernie. By a fortunate freak not long afterwards along came a rather average hurdler with exactly the same name who, when put over steeplechases, burgeoned and flourished until he was one of the best steeplechasers in the country. He is still in training and was second at the Cheltenham Festival this year.

Having found myself – and not for the first time – with no regular income (except for the General Knowledge machine in the Kingston pub next to my office – and then they had to go and change the questions!) I was boasting to Karen the Copywriter about this astonishingly successful system I had developed for winning on the horses when she muttered:

'Don't boast about it – market it!'

Karen the Copywriter has a great nose for such things and is a walking embodiment (or, in her Renault Turbo, a driving embodiment) of opportunism. What Thatcher preached, Karen practised, and she has outlasted the ex-prime minister.

So market it I did.

All-Weather Racing

I had had some experience of racing, having been an owner in the mid-1960s when Francis Ford Coppola had just made a movie of my second novel and money seemed for spending. I had registered my colours, maroon and grey, bought an Irish mare named Anac Cuan and seen her win – eventually – a novice hurdle at Bangor on Dee. The locals had plunged on a locally trained animal and I led Anac Cuan in to a chorus of silent disapproval. Ever since I had been intrigued by horses and betting and had watched with mounting horror while the bookmakers made it ever more difficult for the punter to break even. When I made my first bets in the sixties there was no betting tax and you could get one-third the odds for a place even in a race with an odds-on favourite. Well, it was taking candy from a baby!

In its early editions – as I write this, the fourteenth has just returned from the printers – Ernie employed the simple device of identifying those races which favourites are most likely to win and applying a staking plan to those races. It was – and remains – a solidly based plan and, when rigidly adhered to, profitable; but dull. If people are coughing up good money (is there any other kind?) for a System which promises to turn every barrow boy into an Onassis, every secretary into Ivana Trump, they want something better than favourites, favourites, favourites on which to win, win, win. But I have digressed from the A-Board.

The initial plan dreamed up by Karen the Copywriter and me was to take our first edition of Uncle Ernie's System to a handful of race-meetings (we selected seven) during the month of January, set up our trestle-table behind our A-Board, and watch as the money rolled in. The System ran to a dozen pages, and was printed in Winchester for 45p a copy. We planned to retail it at £10, which seemed like a handy mark-up. That January was the most relentlessly pluvious anyone could remember. When at last the rains stopped the fog arrived. At Ascot where we had planned to sell our copies in the official bookshop because the authorities would have baulked at an A-Board and a trestle-table, the racing was called off when the fog descended before the first race. All the other meetings were cancelled, except only for Fontwell. Fontwell had sentimental associations for Karen the Copywriter: they had named a race after her father. The official who showed us to our boggy pitch was genial. He seemed almost reluctant to take the modest amount the racecourse had quoted to us, which would see us in profit if we were able to sell maybe a half-dozen Ernies.

In the event the weather was so foul, the racegoers so sparse and so disconsolate, that we sold only the one copy at a knockdown price of £3, and that to the official who had admitted us, and he bought it more from pity (I could tell) than any confident hope of profit.

Shortly afterwards we concluded that if trestle-tables and A-Boards were not the answer we should set our sights higher. I secured a shop in the shopping village at Aintree races for the Grand National meeting. A week or two before the event I panicked. What if nobody bought any Ernies? There we would be with a whole shop full of racing systems, and no money to pay our expenses. I rang around the publishers. Did they have any racing books – preferably National Hunt – which they were prepared to let us have on a sale-or-return basis? They had, they would and they did. Before the meeting was over we had sold out of racing books, and had also sold several pictures, which a local artist brought us. We learned an important lesson: when people have just won money from the bookmakers they will buy anything, anything, that is, except Uncle Ernie. When we packed up to go home we found we had over £1800 in cash – and a car full of Ernies. The message was clear. We would turn to direct mail.

The Numbers Game

Statistics fascinate me; always have. Figures are poetry. If, for example, you take the number 142,857, which appears unremarkable, it hums with possibilities. Multiply it by two and it becomes 285,714, the same sequence of digits; multiplied by three, it becomes 428,571, by four it becomes 571,428, by five 714,285, by six 857,142. In each case the same digits in the same sequence. Multiply it by seven and you get 999,999. It has blown a fuse. Beautiful.

An accountant showed me a roulette system which is Byronic in its wit. I like the notion that, while it is profitless to try to predict which number that little silver ball will favour with its attentions, it is certain that one from any block of, say, six numbers will crop up entirely regularly during a night of roulette. Such principles (the projection into the future of lessons learnt from the past) are sound ones to be guided by, and form the mathematical basis of Uncle Ernie's System. For with similar conditions, and removed external elements, horses are astonishingly predictable. They run beautifully to form. All that one needs to do is carefully quantify these variables, and Bob (or Ernie) is your uncle.

The Real World

Advertised by direct mail, the System flourished. I became familiar with, even fond of, some of my clients. There were several peers of the realm. There was a man in prison who was only allowed to send one letter a month and chose to write to Uncle Ernie. He was using his time usefully, he claimed, by studying form, so that when he came out he would never have to turn to crime again. Did I have a dog-eared or coffee-stained copy I could let him have cheap? It would take him a long time to sew enough mailbags to raise £15. I had plenty of dog-eared, coffee-stained Ernies. I sent him one.

There is a woman of eighty-five with an arthritic hip. She writes me chatty letters with each new order. Her latest told me she has finally found a suitable nursing home, but can't get out to the betting shop, though she still manages to have the odd bet, and doesn't know what she would do if she couldn't. She finds Ernie helpful.

One correspondent noticing my unusual name (which as the law requires appears on all publicity) asked whether I was any relation to Henry Benedictus, with whom many years before he had had a happy business relationship. I put them in touch.

Perhaps the most touching letter read (in part): 'My dear brother Charles, to whom I gave Uncle Ernie's system for the 1991 Flat Season, died last month. But he had a very successful Ascot. I like to think that he was helped by your booklet.'

One of the pleasures of running a mail-order racing system is that those who do well from it are desperate to share their gratitude with you and write in extravagant terms. Those who do less well dislike the world to know that they have been rash and ill-advised and keep the information to themselves. I receive many more commendations than criticisms, but the criticisms are colourfully couched. A recent one threatened me with used tampons, though it was unclear precisely what he intended to do with them. It is worth remarking though that the letters I have received as Editor of BBC *Radio Readings* have been even more extravagant. One World Service listener who failed to enjoy a week of Bram Stoker horror stories promised to daub the wall with messages written in the blood of my children.

Ringing the Changes

It was while I was at the BBC – and Ernie was becoming a nice little earner, though onerous – that I conceived the dotty idea of starting one of those 0898 telephone lines which disfigure the pages of the racing press with fantastic claims and even more fantastic promises. One of them was recently hauled over the coals by a press watchdog committee for advertising that 'this One Simply Cannot Lose'. Inevitably it did. His defence was superbly imaginative. He claimed that the newspaper had omitted the quotation marks with which he had surrounded his claim, so that it no longer appeared to be the advice *he* had received from one of his spies. Ernie made no such fabulous promises. I would stay up until the small and not so small hours working out my selections and wake myself up at seven in time to get them on line. We had some successes and the Ernie phone-line was showing a small profit, when I decided to do some sums. I divided the income I was receiving from the phone-line (about £35 a week) by the hours I was spending (about seventeen and a half a week), and concluded, taking into account my poor performance at managerial meetings, my galloping lassitude, and the probability that each Ernie message was likely to shorten my life by a week, that my phone service was carrying altruism too far. Uncle Ernie's phone-line was disconnected.

Uncle's Method

The questions most frequently asked of me by those who know about my *alter ego* are: 'Does it actually work?' and 'If it works why do you bother to market it?' I find it hard to answer these questions. The System has become so sophisticated, containing different *modi operandi* for different customers (those with plenty of time to spend, those in a hurry and so forth) that it is no longer possible to say whether it actually works. I believe it does. I do know that the last Royal Ascot meeting was a triumph for Uncle Ernie, and that the last Cheltenham Festival meeting was not. But overall, day in, day out? To keep the statistics in a businesslike form would take longer than I care to spend, and I prefer to believe what my customers write to me.

> dear sir or madam
> on getting your uncle ernies guide to the jumps i studied it for some time before trying my luck and uncle ernies method so a fortnight ago i put on a ten pound three horse roll up. they all won 175 pounds so this week i tried again 10 pound roll up three horses they all won this time i won 650 pounds in a month i have won 775 pounds thanks to uncles method now could you please send me a copy of uncles flat raceing book enclosed is acheck for 10 pounds
> yours gratefully

or

> Two copies please. I am fed up with my married daughter borrowing my copy when she comes to visit!!

or

'THANK YOU VERY MUCH FOR THE 100/1 66/1 20/1
16/1 ALSO A LOT OF WINNERS FROM TELEPHONE
SERVICES'

(This last message was something of a puzzler. If my correspondent
had found a winner at 100/1 through using Uncle Ernie's System
he was cleverer than I was. I had entirely missed it.)

How might Uncle Ernie expand in the future? That splendid
organization, Amnesty International, has always argued that its success will only be complete when it has put itself out of business. I
suppose that the time might come when bookmakers, noticing that
their client was carrying the latest edition of Uncle Ernie's System,
would nudge one another and say: 'Oh my God, it's another of
them Ernie freaks. Quick, Solly, close the satchel, let's get the hell
outa here.'

Unfortunately this pipe-dream will remain a pipe-dream because
bookmaking is no longer a gambling profession at all. I would
advise a teenager that to become (or to marry) a bookmaker is a
great deal safer than to become (or to marry) an estate agent or a
politician (although with a less active sexual life). And I would
further remark that since the bookmakers are now able, with their
vast resources, to manipulate the market – and they do – they can
ensure that they need never lose – and they don't. They have
become as infallible as the Pope. The most that Ernie can become
is a nagging irritation to them, brought up at board meetings perhaps under Any Other Business, in which case they would probably
decide that what is necessary is to shade the odds on all Ernie
selections. By then the Big Four bookmakers will probably have
become so essential to the economy that their directors will all be
Companions of Honour, and their sponsorship the only thing which
keeps the British sporting scene intact.

When my conscience pricks me that by marketing Ernie I am
encouraging the most vulnerable members of society to become
even more vulnerable, I console myself by believing that gamblers
are born not made and that – to put it sententiously – Uncle Ernie
will help them to gamble a little more successfully. The other day

my son, coming upon some advertising copy for the System, went into peals of hysterical laughter. I asked him the cause.

'This,' he said waving the paper. It proclaimed 'Winning becomes a Way of Life with Uncle Ernie!' I certainly shan't be leaving the business to him.

Back to Basics

JULIAN WILSON

I often wonder nowadays whether, had I been born thirty years later, I should have ever considered making a career as a racing journalist. So much has changed in the past thirty years . . . how much of it has been for the good? There is no doubt that British racing is facing a crisis of identity. The pace of 'progress' in the past ten years has seen more change than in the previous hundred years.

Oh for the days of 1953 when your correspondent first became a regular 'school-holidays' racegoer, having followed the sport on a day-to-day basis from the age of nine. Every day I would write my racing selections neatly in an exercise book. There was time a-plenty for reflection. Rarely, if ever, were there more than two race meetings on a weekday. The horses were familiar and likewise the jockeys.

There were 204 flat-race meetings in 1953, and just over 4500 horses ran one or more races. In 1993, by the end of the Turf season there had been 431 meetings and over 8000 participants. How can any serious student cope with so many horses, and so much racing? And this ignores the 499 meetings run under National Hunt Rules.

From the sensible mix of two meetings a weekday and three on a Saturday has developed a gorgon-like monster of a fixture list, with over 1100 individual days' racing scheduled for 1995. With the burgeoning curse of all-weather track racing, several Saturdays now carry up to seven meetings.

Newspapers groan under the extra burden on the busiest sporting day of the week; shrewd trainers take avoiding action with competitive horses; and normally analytical punters become confused and cross-eyed. Only the betting shop addicts feast on the endless repetitive ten-minute fix. There's always the chance of the great escape. Eventually the very last life-belt has floated away . . .

The first radical alteration to the framework of British racing in the 1970s was the centralization of handicapping. This was a fundamental change of direction. In the past, each race meeting was allocated an individual handicapper, whose opinions, notably with two year olds, could vary by several pounds from those of his colleagues. I remember vividly in the early 1960s how a two year old with several entries in nurseries on the Scottish circuit could be allocated weights that would vary by up to twenty-one pounds between Ayr, Bogside and Hamilton Park. Now every horse would have the same handicap figure in every race, stored as a numeral in Wetherby's central computer.

The advantage of the new system was that if an owner wanted to run at Ayr there was no conflict on the grounds that your horse was better handicapped at Bogside. Wherever he ran he ran off the same mark – until he was re-assessed. The down-side was that one could no longer exploit a favourable handicap mark.

Another radical change was that weights in handicaps were raised at the overnight declaration stage, so that the top weight became nine stone seven pounds (or nine stone ten pounds for older horses). This was the death-knell for lightweight jockeys. Weights could rise by anything up to twenty-one pounds.

In earlier days the weight that was allotted by the handicapper remained the weight that the horse carried. During the coughing epidemic of 1969, the weights carried in the valuable Blacknest Handicap at Ascot on the day of the King George VI & Queen Elizabeth Stakes were as follows:

Woolley	4–7–10 (incl. 10 lb extra)
Big Valley	4–7–7
Dale Cross	5–7–7
Terence	5–7–0
Blazing Scent	10–7–0

*   *   *

Today, those weights would have risen by thirty-one pounds overnight. (Penalties are not included in assessment.)

It was one of many modifications to frustrate the art of the professional trainer. In earlier days, the trainer would know at least
two weeks in advance the precise weight that his horse would carry
and prepare the horse for the specific target. He would also make an
early engagement of his chosen jockey. Now, under the abominable
five-day entry system, introduced in 1989, a trainer no longer knows
the entries, let alone the weights to be carried, until the week of
the race.

The racehorse, once a finely tuned athlete, has become akin to
a motorbike ticking over, waiting to be pulled out of the garage. And
now they have built racecourses ideal for these equine motorbikes to
hurtle round. They are called All-Weather Tracks.

Meanwhile, the breed of professional backer who travelled from
course to course has become an extinct species. It becomes harder
and harder to win.

The introduction of the All-Weather Track in 1989 was the
most revolutionary, or retrograde, development in British racing –
depending upon your point of view – since the war. The original
stated purpose of what many regard as a desecration of British
racing was 'to offset the losses to the Levy caused by abandonments
during the winter period'.

The Jockey Club notice continued 'Most of these normally occur
during the months of January, February and March, and mainly
due to waterlogging. The Levy Board has calculated that abandonments cost racing, in lost levy, at least £1.2 million every year.'

The Muddle family, father and son, Ron and Richard, have been
the pioneers of All-Weather Track racing, and have exploited their
opportunity superbly. Lingfield (now sold), Southwell and Wolverhampton have all been transformed by the Muddles' building and
marketing expertise – with substantial assistance from the
Horserace Betting Levy Board.

But the original concept was swept aside long ago. Now All-
Weather Track racing takes place all year round, and, in the case
of Wolverhampton, under floodlights all year round. The racing
is mediocre in the extreme. Who cares if Samson Agonistes
beats Simmie's Special today . . . or next week . . . or the week
after? The races constitute equine roulette. By no stretch of the

imagination could anyone claim that it constitutes 'improving the breed of racehorses'. But it continues to be heavily subsidized by the Levy Board.

Meanwhile, the perception of British racing, as evidenced by the sand sport, is of a degeneration to the level of racing at Cahokia Downs or Rockingham Park in the United States.

Pity the unfortunate American owner who, to escape the endless monotony of racing on dirt 'back home', comes to England's green and pleasant land ... only to be told by his English trainer that his horse is running at Wolverhampton on Monday night! In the view of many, this obsession with racing on sand should be halted before it take serious root.

The principal benefactors to British racing are overseas owners – notably from the Middle East – and race sponsors. Both are attracted by the elitism and excellence of British racing. It remains 'The Sport of Kings'. It would be hugely damaging to British racing to see it sink to the social level of greyhound racing.

It was only last year that Prince Khaled Abdullah, owner of three English Classic winners in 1993, confessed that it was the glamour of racing, as portrayed on BBC Television, that attracted him to the British sport.

'I used to watch racing on television when I came to England with my family to rent a London house for the summer. I got very excited over those TV races and thought it was something I would like to get into.'

The Maktoum family of Dubai had similar sentiments. Now they are the most powerful force in European racing. The packaging of the British sport remains of paramount importance.

There is also a sinister side to All-Weather racing, especially over hurdles. When four horses were killed in a single week at Lingfield and Southwell during 1994, the perception grew that the sport provided unacceptable risks. On 25 February the remainder of the 1994 programme was abandoned.

Many jockeys had rung the alarm bells from Day One. Whereas soft and yielding turf affords horse and rider the chance to minimize injury, the resilience of Fibresand prevents the necessary sliding motion for a falling horse. The effect is that, at the point of impact, the rear end of the horse tends to be travelling faster than the front end. The resultant jar damages or breaks limbs. The same process applies to a falling jockey, who, instead of sliding or rolling, can be brought to a jarring halt.

By the end of February, the whisper calling for the abolition of jumping on All-Weather tracks had become a roar. There was also a serious complaint over the toxic anti-freeze material used in the Equitrack surface at Lingfield Park. The Sevenoaks permit-holder, John Panvert, claimed that one of his horses had been poisoned by sand and oil entering his horse's bloodstream through the pores of the skin. The horse suffered acute swollen limbs, and six weeks later it had to be destroyed.

What is undeniable is that jockeys have become American clones by racing hell-for-leather from pillar-to-post. The traditional skills of British race riding are swept aside. This is why women riders enjoy considerably more success on sand than on grass. Furthermore, the suicidal speed over hurdles is undoubtedly a contributory factor to the number of fatal falls.

The All-Weather Track is just one symptom of the never-mind-the-quality-feel-the-width attitude now prevalent in British racing. There are several others.

Back in those hallowed days of 1953, no trainer had more than seventy horses in his stable. The most successful was Sir Jack Jarvis, who won races with thirty-nine horses. In 1993, Richard Hannon ran 207 separate horses during the season and won with 111 of them! John Gosden ran 128 horses, Paul Cole 120, Michael Stoute 118 and Henry Cecil 108, and there were plenty of horses in these stables that *didn't* run.

Overheads in racing stables increase year by year. Many trainers import Canadian oats at great expense; mineral supplements are widely used; several trainers have specially built covered rides and equine swimming pools. There are veterinary units with solariums, magnetopulse machines, jacuzzis, nebulizers and ultra-sound gadgets. Others have horse walkers, and All-Weather canters.

The racing office, which in 1953 comprised one secretary with a typewriter, and the requirement to make entries on one day a week, now has two secretaries, Prestel, a telex, a fax machine, two telephones and in some cases a computer. Several trainers are linked to the Satellite Information System, at a cost of up to £9000 per annum. So racing has become an increasingly complicated and cost-intensive business.

None of this takes into account the most important factor of all, the stable work-force. Happily, the days of slave labour have passed by. In 1994, the Grade A (Skilled) National Minimum Rate for experienced stable staff, working a forty-hour week, rose to £154.62; not a fortune, but boosted by generous overtime for weekend working.

However, whereas until recently a stable-lad was expected to look after just two horses, nowadays the norm is one lad to *four* horses. Small wonder that corners are cut, and the standard of grooming compares unfavourably with what it was in the past. Often, when lads are away at the races with the horses they look after, the ratio of lads to horses in the stable is one to six. Nor can the trainer afford to allow his staff an extra 'overnight'. Even from Newcastle and Redcar, the horsebox must return on the day of the race – often arriving home after midnight.

Small wonder the professional punters scratch their head and wonder at the inconsistency and lack of resilience of the modern racehorse. Meanwhile the betting conveyor belt trundles on . . .

Another insuperable enemy of the modern-day punter is disease. It was in the late sixties that the first major scare emerged, with a threatened outbreak of African Horse Sickness. Almost every year in the past twenty-five there has been some outbreak of coughing, influenza or viral infection. Nowadays, it is mandatory for a racehorse to receive a course of influenza injections before he is permitted to race. Some trainers inject their horses every six months. Yet nothing seems able to stop the spread of disease.

Every spring, as certain as bluebells, there will be tales of coughing and virus. It spreads like wildfire through the leading training centres. Horse transport and racecourse stables are perennial vehicles for infections. The injections, quite simply, do not work. There is no limit to the transport of disease. In the spring of 1994 it even spread from Britain to the United Arab Emirates.

Often the infection is well-concealed, and impossible to detect until a horse has been under stress. At the same time certain trainers are economical with the truth for fear of losing horses and wealthy patrons.

In the late 1980s the northern trainer Steve Norton suffered a crippling outbreak of equine virus, which lasted on and off for almost two years. By the time his stable was free of infection, his stable strength was reduced from sixty horses to barely twenty.

The 'virus' has created yet another minefield for serious punters. So what else can happen to damage the sport that we love, erratic, overhorsed and underfunded as it has become?

The year 1994 was a vital one for horseracing. It was the first year of control of the sport by a new body, the British Horseracing Board . . . the dawn of a new age. But where were the great panaceas for success? It was soon made clear that two ambitions stood head and shoulders above the rest: the creation of a new, million-pound Superbet, and the earliest-possible introduction of regular Sunday racing.

Of all the popular misconceptions in racing in the 1990s, the conviction that racing on the Lord's Day is the answer to racing's prayers, is perhaps the worst thought-out and most misunderstood. The superficial success of racing on Sunday in Ireland has been grossly distorted. It has been achieved at considerable cost. In the early days, the profit and loss account made bizarre reading. The demands of the relevant unions made a nonsense of financial viability. The second realization by the Irish was that no racecourse can sustain racing on Saturday *and* Sunday, by attracting a large crowd on both days. When racing takes place at The Curragh on these two days, very often the attendance on Saturday is no more than three thousand.

Sunday racing would be a five-day wonder. It would be suicidal to compete with the other major European countries with prestige racing. The present clash between the Budweiser Irish Derby at The Curragh and the Grand Prix de Paris at Longchamp has already given an indication of how thinly runners and resources can be stretched.

Quite simply, Sunday is the prime sporting day of the week in France, Germany, Italy, Spain and now Ireland. All except Germany are predominantly Roman Catholic countries. Saturday has always been Britain's sporting day. Cricket, soccer, rugby and racing all stage their major events on a Saturday. It is part of our heritage. To ask the substantial work-force that generates horseracing to work on a Sunday would, in my opinion, be morally and ethically wrong. Whether motivated by religion, family values, laziness or exhaustion, the Englishman chooses to spend Sunday at home. Above all, there is the element of the family unit. At a time when parental control has disintegrated to the extent that ten-year-old boys can abduct and murder toddlers, it seems vital that families should pull together and restore family values. That cannot happen if on most Sundays a father is compelled to go to work.

Furthermore, almost every married man who works in stables has a working wife. Stablemen's wages, as related earlier, are insufficient to accommodate a family group. Constant separation, linked with a seven-day working week, brings on increasing stress. There is no surer formula for the break-up of a marriage. This is one reason why journalists have appalling matrimonial track records.

And the racegoer? After two or three Sunday evenings spent in stationary traffic, with twenty-mile tail-backs of weekend drivers returning to the big cities, on top of a photo-finish reverse in the last race . . . next week the zoo may be more attractive.

The great attraction of racing at Longchamp is the proximity to the city centre: a family lunch is only ten minutes away. Likewise at Deauville, just five minutes' walk from the sea-front. A racecourse in Hyde Park would be a perfect vehicle for Sunday racing. But there isn't one.

So the great ship Racing continues to scramble sideways like a disoriented crab. It remains underfinanced and misdirected. Unless someone grabs the tiller with a firm hand, the great ship looks to be headed for the rocks.

It wasn't the greatest political concept of 1994, but, in my view, the need of horseracing is to get 'Back to Basics'.

First Past the Post

WILLIAM POWELL

Derby Day 1960: my best friend was quite clear that Scobie Breasley would win, that Alcaeus was the one to back. For me it was to be Lester Piggott, not his great rival. Piggott and St Paddy came home first and my life-long affair with the Turf started. Each day the papers were studied, devoured: by the end of the 1960 season L. Piggott had been replaced in my pantheon of heroes by N. Murless. For by now Trevor Bailey was largely forgotten (1959 had been his great season anyway); from now on racing was the sport to be followed; cricket, by contrast, was in terminal decline.

Every horse from then until now – and from now to eternity – to emerge from the Warren Place Stables was, and always will be, a sure winner. The pedigrees were analyzed, usually back for a hundred years and more, the form was carefully noted. Everything was studied, committed to memory. Even twenty years later the weather of every day of summer throughout the 1960s could be recalled merely by remembering which Murless runner had been at the races: its performance effortlessly recollected. In the old days schoolboys learnt poetry, a thousand lines at a time; entire Shakespeare plays, Milton or Tennyson were learnt by rote. For me it was racehorse pedigrees – not all of them, just the Warren Place ones. Such disciplining of the memory has served me well.

Each year, of course, with the coming of spring came also the confident expectation of a new champion whose performance would shine even more brightly than those of existing champions. Crepello and Petite Etoile were obviously only intended to be the fore-runners, preparing the way for even greater equine athletes. The agony and bitter despair which accompanied the cruel destruction of Pinturiscio in 1961; the shattering realization that St Paddy, although a thoroughly good Derby winner, was not the best, and then the dashed expectation of glory from Follow Suit, Alan Adare and Casabianca and so many others. How could Soft Angels fail to start in her three year old race? (She did at least redeem herself, if not on the Turf, then at least at stud, by being the mother to Doubly Sure.) Each spring brought renewed confidence and expectation of triumphs to come, though these often stretched existing friendships to the very limits. Even today, one of my old pals always starts a conversation by reminding me of Yaroslav. Of course he had lost money; not so for me, for the betting side of racing was the least interesting. Just as Tottenham Hotspur were and are expected to win each match, by a wide margin, so it remains a crushing sadness that the Warren Place runners continue to enjoy a less than 100 per cent strike rate. Quite inexplicable.

So I have always been throughout a thoroughly biased observer, always partisan, unreasonable and insufferable, because always able to produce convincing reasons why the fancy of others could not possibly be expected to win. In racing at least, I always, like Denis Healey in politics, won the argument and was usually wrong even when winning. What fun it has been. There is no more stirring sight than a brave horse galloping for the line, particularly when bottomless reservoirs of courage and speed are produced at the point of challenge. Reference Point is today underestimated, but how he unleashed those energies. For many the great sweeping run from behind, as with Sir Ivor or Dancing Brave, is the supreme style of a great horse. Maybe. Slip Anchor galloped down to Derby glory from the front and in doing so now remains the only unchallenged winner of the great race in modern times, for not a single one of those following him was able to strike up any kind of challenge – and it must be remembered that the runner-up, Law Society, was no slouch. How could he ever be beaten? Old Vic at Chantilly – and what a stirring battle it was – went down to such gallant defeat in the King George VI & Queen Elizabeth Stakes when beaten by his stable companion Belmez: the wrong horse won but at least it was Warren Place first and second. Nor should the fillies be forgotten: Sir Noel Murless was the finest trainer ever of classic fillies and Henry Cecil is establishing a respectable claim to be the runner up of this particular division – as Oh So Sharp, Diminuendo and Indian Skimmer have all demonstrated. So there have been sufficient champions among the long list of disappointments to excite the mind, stir the soul and release the adrenaline each spring. Oh how February and March each year drag: the coming of the Craven meeting is the most important objective of the first months in any new year.

Of course it is the *most important* objective, not merely the most important racing objective. Gone are the days when the Prime Minister could, like Lord Rosebery, own the winner of a Derby, or that Parliament would not sit on Derby Day. At least, Douglas Hurd and Michael Howard amongst the most recent Home Secretaries have visited Epsom – and who was that photographed at Epsom in 1993 shortly after being sacked as Chancellor of the Exchequer? Yes, politicians do continue to support the Turf. At the present time several, through partnerships and syndicates, own part of a horse: none however belongs to the Jockey Club. It was not always so.

There is a famous story of a Tory MP, grandee and Jockey Club member, who was without a pair (i.e. a member of the opposing party who would agree to stay away from any Divisions, thus preserving the government of the day's majority). He consulted the form book, studied the runners and identified a most agreeable Labour MP, formerly a miner who clearly found racing far more interesting than politics. There was one drawback: he already had a pair – a fine Tory with an excellent war record. Convention has it that to steal a colleague's pair is an unforgivable Parliamentary offence. However, cometh the hour, cometh the man. An invitation was issued to join him in his box at Epsom on Derby Day; before the first race a discreet word advised that he had a very good tip so he had placed a £10 bet for his guest. It won. The winnings were paid out. So also all the other tips of the day – each a winner – and the winnings were paid over – though not once was the name of any of these tips ever mentioned. At the end of a splendid afternoon pairing arrangements were altered. So even for Jockey Club members political expediency can be more important than good manners.

There always used to be a group of Labour MPs, usually from the North, who made a respectable living out of the bookmakers. Their numbers today are rather depleted as social workers have replaced the old trade unionists – but there are still one or two. Enter the House of Commons library during the afternoon or evening and Ceefax is still consulted for up-to-date odds and results. The *Racing Calendar* is still taken by Library, though it may be some time again before any Member would include in his entry to *The Times Guide to the House of Commons* as did the MP for Croydon North in 1950 'one of his horses won the Great Metropolitan Handicap in April 1948. He owns a farm in Kenya.' The *Sporting Life* and the *Racing Post* are available in the Members' tearoom. Alas they are too little consulted.

For the truth is that nowadays newspapers carry two pages of predictions. The front page, usually the work of the political correspondents, predicts the future of politics, scarcely ever bothering to report past real events rather than speculation as to what might happen at some stage in the future. At least in the old days when there was no news the sub-editors would produce a spectacular headline 'Ominous Silence in Bulgaria'. But it is to the back pages that we must turn if we are really to make an objective assessment of tipping as against results. For most of the time racing journalists have a far better record for predictions than any of their political counterparts. Not infrequently they also write rather better English. If only they would change places! For one MP at least the day still starts with the racing press, not the more conventional reading material of the politician. I am now too old to change a third of a century's habits and the racing press is always far more interesting.

The modern MP has one other privilege: the All Party Racing Committee. At 6 p.m. on the first Tuesday of each month when Parliament is in session, we assemble in an upstairs committee room, Lords and Commons together, to hear a guest speaker, to discuss our annual visit to the races and to savour the fact that the Mother of Parliaments still contains a huge body of racing knowledge and experience. It is, above all, their Lordships who make the occasion so special. Mostly they are silent, often giving the impression that they were steeplechase jockeys before the Great War: some only come up to London to attend the committee before returning to their stables or to their studies. Above all, the committee provides the opportunity to take the political temperature of racing at Westminster. The reduction in on-course betting duty, evening opening of betting shops, VAT and bloodstock, Sunday racing and betting, the future of the Tote – all of these have been thoroughly canvassed at committee. We like to think we have some influence. Senior Stewards, Chairmen and Secretaries of various racing bodies, bookmakers, even John McCririck, have addressed us. Luca Cumani has told us how bad things are, while others have been a great deal more cheerful. There you see Nicholas Budgen, formerly a respectable jockey, tease Lord Carnarvon; Lord Wyatt, Dennis Turner MP, Lord Plummer, Lord Huntingdon, Sir Geoffrey Johnson Smith and many others are regular attenders. Of all the Parliamentary Committees which it is my privilege to attend, none gives me greater pleasure and enjoyment. Thank God for the All Party Racing Committee.

In the recent past the House of Lords has spent a day debating the racing industry, thanks to Lord Donoughue, and the list of speakers was far longer than that for almost any other debate in recent years – only the War Crimes Bill and the debate approving the ordination of women to the priesthood of the Church of England have attracted greater interest. The debate was spoken of weeks after it had been concluded. That cannot be said of very much Parliamentary discussion. The House of Commons Select Committee on Home Affairs investigated the horseracing industry and their reports played a major part in bringing about the changes in the organization and management of racing, which are now well under way. So far they have been less influential over the privatization of the Tote. That remains a long way away. In a very real sense it can be claimed that the present government has consistently been more helpful to the racing industry than to any other sport. It was Lord Whitelaw who insisted upon the establishment of the HRC when he was Home Secretary; it was Lord Lawson who reduced on-course betting duty just before the 1987 general election; and the long campaign over the prospect of remarkably different VAT rates in France and Ireland as against our own much higher rate was ultimately successful. Racing owes more to Sir Charles Morrison and to Mr James Paice than it may realize.

For the fact is we have much in the British racing scene for which we should be very thankful. Britain enjoys the most competitive racing, in conditions of great variety and frequently with much beauty. The results of our races are not preordained by the choice of Andre Fabre or Dermot Weld, when they decide which of their very many horses should run in a particular event. The betting public is well served and racing is as clean as anywhere. The bookmakers see to that: corrupt betting would lead to the collapse of something which would decidedly not be in their interests. Of course, they are often abused but we owe them more than it is usually fashionable to concede. Mr Len Cowburn and others have been amongst racing's greatest ambassadors. Of course the grass is always greener on the other side of the hill: it always is, but to this observer British racing is and, God willing, will remain magic.

This has not always, however, been how it is seen by those most intimately involved with the sport. Indeed for the last few years there has been an extraordinary amount of internal debate about the supposed declining quality and standards of British racing by the very people whose livelihood is derived from the sport. I have known Newmarket since the 1950s and today it basks in a prosperity far greater than that of anything which existed two or three decades ago. There are more horses in training, employing more people, with more races being run. The standard and quality of British racing is as high as it has ever been and as high as in any country of the world. The 1960s saw the export of many of the very best mares available from British studs, and the decline of the small owner breeder whose breeding operations have been built up over generations. At Warren Place, back in the 1960s, very few of the horses in training had been purchased at public auction or indeed had been bred outside the United Kingdom. Continuity and stability were the hallmarks of the blood lines passing through all of the nation's leading stables.

Then came the big changes: Lester Piggott became a freelance in controversial circumstances, American breeds started to win all the big races, French prize money was deemed to be more attractive. It was obvious that we could not possibly be expected to hold our own. Above all else the penal rates of capital taxation payable upon death meant that the inheritors of wealth so often had to dispose of their assets in order to meet the unwelcome tax bill.

Not least of the present Conservative government's reforms has been to draw the sting of so much of the absurd and counter-productive burden of these taxes. Yet the racing industry was virtually silent during the campaigns, in which I played a major part, during the 1980s to lower and eliminate death duties, or capital transfer tax or, as it now is, inheritance tax. It would have been much better if the owners and proprietors of those small studs, whose bloodlines stretched back into the nineteenth century, had been far more prominent in explaining to our political masters just how damaging high tax rates and low tax thresholds on capital can be. A small stud owner was merely a small businessman and until the 1980s it was very difficult to pass on intact an inheritance from one generation to another. Yet the improvement of the thoroughbred depended upon continuity and stability in breeding policy. Of course a strong demand for animals at public auction is a necessary part of a healthy system of racing and so are the private stud farms breeding to race their own products. Year after year we have seen the progressive elimination of such farms. It has been disastrous.

Of course, the arrival of Sheikh Mohammad and his brothers, Mr Khaled Abdullah, Prince Fahd Salman and many others from the Middle East began to reverse those trends. The world's leading stallions began to stand in Great Britain and Ireland. The world's best mares were at stud at Newmarket and in Berkshire and elsewhere in the United Kingdom. Yes, indeed, Britain was still the best place to rear and train and race the thoroughbred – just as it always had been. English-trained horses were not only winning the major French races but also challenging for, and sometimes winning, big races in the USA and even Australia.

Whilst the talk remained of securing a larger contribution, through the bookmakers, from the punter to finance British racing, steps were also being taken to improve the facilities at British courses. Yet even today there is still a very long way to go and racing is still not seen, as it should be, as a family sport. Nevertheless it is sustained by small owners frequently of bad horses: bad horses which have little prospect of being able to earn any rate of return at all for their sporting and hopeful patrons. I have one constituent who has owned racehorses since before World War Two and who tells me that she has never owned one which has not come in last in all the races in which her colours have been carried. Increased prize money, whatever its other attractions, would be of precious little advantage to her; but the thrill of her colours being carried combined with the hope that something will be better in the future have sustained her hearty and sporting enthusiasm. We need very many more like her just as we need large crowds, high betting turnover and strong public interest. The improvements I wish to see would all be directed to achieving such results.

The last thing the Turf now needs is a narrow circle of introverted moaners unable and unwilling to welcome the newcomer. If the USA and Hong Kong and other areas of the world are able to generate large crowds and enormous interest in the races so also we should try much more energetically than hitherto. What racing has to offer is a most magnificent spectacle. When set against the beauty and variety of the British racecourses, there is no inherent reason why much larger crowds and much greater excitement should not be generated.

Above all let no one forget that we are talking about the most magnificent of beasts – the horse. Like most of my Parliamentary colleagues I have very few constituents who are more interested in politics than they are in the Turf: not just in the betting shops but also on course the racehorse really does inspire admiration.

They All Hurt

RICHARD PITMAN

It does not matter one jot if a jump jockey happens to be a full brother to the Bishop of Galway, the Turf is no respecter of relationships: he will still hit the ground too often for the good of his ego, his looks or his health.

To a kid in stables the thought of falling is nothing more than part of the job; it even heightens the anticipation of proving that those with visible alterations to their faces were perhaps lacking something between the ears. The initial schooling sessions are never done at racing pace, which only serves to confirm the cocky aspiring champion in his theory that he's cracked the system. The law of averages plays its hand soon enough when it comes to riding in public, however; and the instant of impact, when your body passes the point of no return comes as a sharp reminder that pride does indeed come before a fall.

It all happens so quickly that self-preservation is still fumbling to get into play when the wind is knocked out of the limp excuse for a body and the noise of the other twenty runners going over your prostrate form drowns out the eerie respiratory sounds as the fallen rider fights to refill his violently emptied lungs. For me, it always seemed to sound like something between a large orchestra tuning up and a foxhound with a blackthorn stuck in its snout. To lie there as other half-ton chasers land beside you, depressing the ground just inches from your vital organs or limbs, is a test of your mettle, to say the least. At some point a message screams from somewhere in the depths of the mind to all remaining intact limbs: protect remaining healthy extremities stop. Roll into a ball stop.

This action cannot stop a beating, but it does minimize the damage. After all, it's common sense to reduce the target. What is probably even more important is that when the next kick does connect it has the effect of rolling the football of flesh over a few revolutions. It still hurts, of course, but with any luck it doesn't snap anything.

It is incredibly noisy underneath a large field of racehorses, and this serves to redouble the joy of that beatific sound, pure silence, as the field gallops off into the distance in pursuit of the prize. You undoubtedly hurt in numerous places, but as the coiled body unfurls itself it becomes happily evident that all parts are in full working order – shaken not stirred.

The teeth feel well loosened, and in some cases distinctly dodgy; but who cares? Dentists can do wonders to straighten them: the old flashing smile will soon be back in place.

As the rider, glad to be alive, pulls himself up to his full height to enjoy the feel of a body still in working order, the warning cry from the groundsman comes too late as amateur jockey Mr Brod Munro-Willnot hurtles over the jump totally unaware that there is someone directly in his path. One concedes that being out of contention and trailing the rest by fully two fences is some excuse for looking admiringly at his shadow.

The sudden engulfing by a horse in full flight and landing over a four foot six inch fence comes as something of a shock to someone still congratulating himself for having emerged relatively unscathed. Worse still is the knowledge that the five teeth loosened earlier will now be extracted by tweezers, two from the cleft in the chin, the others via a new dimple in the upper cheek.

At that stage in a young man's career, despite the alterations to his facial looks, reassuring the trainer of his general wellbeing is of paramount importance: there must be no relapsing into a prone position to lament the lost gnashers, for example. Far from it: a bold stride towards the stands is required. With luck it will be sufficient to persuade him against rushing into the changing room to engage another jockey to ride your next booked mount. A decade later, bent, broken, your features generally altered, it can be a very different story, as the rider stays down in the grass while he considers exactly what the next ride *is*. If the brute happens to be a one-eyed mental case with non-existent brakes and steering, the fallen rider will more than likely stay prostrate on the ground long enough to convince the trainer of the need for the speedy engagement of another rider. This doesn't necessarily mean that the rider's nerve has gone, but rather perhaps that he has learned that adjusting the odds in your favour is the best way of keeping the bones on the inside of the skin.

There is no doubt that the more often you fall the better you become at landing. This is because as it happens more often it seems to happen in slower motion. After being warned that any further bouts of concussion would result in a long involuntary holiday, I distinctly remember having a lo-o-o-ong time, between going over my horse's ears and hitting the deck, to think that I must protect the old grey matter. Assuming a neat curled position in mid-flight, I was able to land on the right shoulder with the head tucked safely under one wing. It proved a sound move, for the think tank was still clear when the upside-down motion came to a stop. The only minus about the episode was that my collar-bone had snapped as neatly as a dry stick.

When such injuries happen the stricken jockey does not need the voluntary first-aid person to diagnose the damage. The feel of the two broken bone-ends grating together as you get to your feet tells you all you want to know. At this stage there is often, strangely, no pain to accompany the injury: adrenaline has an anaesthetic effect on the body – but not for long.

The former champion and Grand National winning jockey Graham Thorner was incredibly hard to shift, even when horses made horrendous mistakes. (My belief is that he likes the feel of money so much that he would stick with a fallen horse almost until the skin came off, in the hope that it might find a leg from somewhere and be able to scramble upright again in time to finish a distant third, qualifying Graham for the rider's 5 per cent of the prize.)

At Worcester in a novice chase, going much too fast for safety to get a leading position, Graham's mount hit the top of a jump and failed to get his landing gear out in time. The horse skidded along the ground for twenty yards with the intrepid pilot still in the crouched position. Eventually, as the horse's momentum ran out, it keeled over sideways, depositing the rider on the turf like a dollop of clay, instead of the normal fast ejection that jump jockeys expect when a horse falls.

Unfortunately for Graham, his right foot was still in the stirrup when the horse got to its feet, leaving him dangling upside-down.

The sudden strain on his thin leg snapped it on the pommel of his saddle. At the time this came as a nasty realization, but in hindsight it is clear that it saved his life. When the leg snapped the foot twisted round, freeing it from the grip of the stirrup and thus allowing Thorner's limp body to part from the horse – whose instinct had spurred it on to chase the disappearing runners. Had his leg not broken so violently he would have been dragged along by the galloping horse, with the result that his body would have been swung beneath his mount's belly, into the path of its flailing hoofs.

Mercifully that did not happen, and, as it happened at the fence in front of the stand, I was able to be by his side as Graham took stock of his plight. Sitting in the wet grass, with the sole of his right riding boot actually facing him, Graham said, 'I think I've twisted my ankle.' It was only a few minutes later, when the pain flooded up and down from the break, that he got the full story. It defies logic, but after such an experience as that, the superstitious rider still continued to ride in his 'lucky' underpants, the pair he had worn when powering home in the 1972 Grand National (on Well To Do, trained by Tim Forster).

It was far easier to hoodwink the medics in those days, and as all jump jockeys are mad keen to get back in the saddle for the dubious pleasure of doing the same thing all over again, it came as no surprise when Thorner over-ruled the X-rays showing his break still only partially healed, by jumping off the consultant's desk. Needless to say, he made sure the good leg took all the weight of the landing, and was passed fit to ride. That would not work these days, I'm glad to say.

It is almost as scary to be on a horse that gallops right over the top of a fallen rider. Horses will go to enormous lengths to avoid someone lying on the ground, even when at full stretch landing after a jump. Incredibly, they find hidden reserves to alter their arc in mid-flight, and they will do so provided the body is well tucked up in a ball. The very speed at which this happens means that a horse cannot avoid a collision if a jockey is running for safety or is lying full-length on the ground. It takes more bottle to roll up tightly than to run when every nerve is screaming to the brain to spur the limbs into action. Sometimes a collision is inevitable even when the fallen rider is bunched, and both the approach and the crunch are unpleasant, for the result is out of your hands. When you are being forced over another body there is an awful void as you wait for the sickening sound of impact – which resembles the noise a dead pig makes when the butcher throws it on to the slab for jointing.

There is an old saying among jump jockeys. 'Keep your heart on the landing side of the jumps. When it's left behind on take-off it's time to look for less arduous work.' This of course can lead to an occasional unseating, prompting onlookers to think the hapless jockey is either crooked or useless. It happens in the Grand National most years, as horses stop without warning, in, literally, the stride in which they are supposed to become airborne. When this happens momentum causes the rider to continue in his intended path, often leaping the fence in the crouched sitting position – just without the equine partner underneath.

Amazingly, luck holds more often than not, especially since body protectors and crash helmet became mandatory – though arms, legs, the face and buttocks are still vulnerable. After crunching a mate, or even a rival for that matter, the sight of him struggling to his feet is worth everything. In the jumping game there is a camaraderie pretty well unknown elsewhere these days. Mick Fitzgerald had his face trodden on in early 1994, only to find it gave him more understanding of horses' discomfort. Having agreed to have his nasal airways cleared at the time of recovery, he remembers vividly both the horrible feeling of choking and the pain as a scope forced its way through the gunge obstructing the passage. 'When I think of all the times I've held a horse while the vet scoped it, without feeling any sympathy, I'm ashamed,' he said.

The end-of-season statistics never fully tell the story, because a fair proportion of failures to keep the bottom in the saddle are because of bad luck or other people's actions. In the 1975 Grand National Andy Turnell went to Becher's Brook on Charles Dickens, riding with as short a stirrup leather as Lester Piggott uses on the flat. He met the formidable obstacle on a good stride, pivoted correctly as the pair descended and rapidly let the reins slip through his fingers as he sat back over the horse's quarters to allow for the big drop on landing. Sadly, his grasp failed to stop at the buckle end of the reins, allowing the rider to do a double somersault over his mount's tail. With the world upside down Andy grabbed at anything and everything to save himself, which, unfortunately for Paul Kelleway, happened to be his arm just as he landed safely over the fearsome jump. The result of this coupling saw Turnell and Kelleway sitting in the grass watching their horses disappearing towards Canal Turn. What Kelleway said to Turnell has not been saved for posterity on account of its unprintability. Such happenings, or falls at early fences, in any big race, always leave the fallen cavaliers with an empty feeling, in the knowledge that it will be a whole year before they can have another crack at it.

Conversely – and it's especially relevant in the light of the much talked-about incident in 1994 when Richard Dunwoody received a fourteen-day ban for barging Adrian Maguire out of a minor Nottingham contest – the jockeys do actually pull rivals back into the saddle if possible, instead of giving them a nudge in the direction of the ground. They all know they are relatively safe while riding, but that anything, including death, can await those on the ground.

There is usually sympathy in abundance after a fall, but one of the first successful woman trainers used to round on riders – probably because of relief that they were still in one piece. (I'm giving her the benefit of the doubt after twenty years.) Two occasions come to mind. When a chaser decided to take the more difficult route through the much larger wing of a fence, instead of going over it, at Fakenham, I ended up lying, winded, across the wooden structure, and was still impaled high above the ground when the trainer strode purposefully up to the base, only to shake the upright post until I fell off at her feet, compounding the original injury. She was far from pleased, and in the ensuing verbal roasting doubts about my parentage were the least of the aspersions she cast.

The other occasion arose when I was going for a touch (racing slang for a gamble) at the now-defunct racecourse at Wye. The horse made every yard of the running, jumped like a stag and still held pole position going into the last bend. Sadly the adverse camber of the course and the fact that the horse had the homing instincts of a racing pigeon prompted it to hang violently towards the stables in the opposite direction to the way the course went. You don't need to be a genius to surmise that the combination of speed being diverted violently on an adverse camber saw the beast slip up in a heap with the race at his mercy and the gamble as good as landed.

When such a departure takes place the resultant ejection sends the pilot skywards rather than forwards, so I landed over the running rails in the centre of the course, winded, convulsing and unable to move as my back had been put out. It must have looked quite serious to onlookers, who were no doubt privately thinking spinal injuries were the most likely, but the bold trainer knew exactly why my limp body was twitching, and kicked me without ceremony off the electrified sheep wire that guarded the course.

Philip Blacker, who is now a world-renowned sculptor and also a member of the Jockey Club, had an amazing near-miss when a horse's steel racing plate sliced across his testicle casing, exposing the contents to the general public and almost ensuring that his then unplanned children Dan and Stephanie were no more than wishful thinking. This awful injury happened at Newton Abbot in Devon, enabling the hapless Blacker to stay on at the Palace Hotel over the weekend, after being put back together and stitched up as good as new – albeit rather swollen. The doctor prescribed plenty of wading in the sea to reduce the swelling and to promote the healing process, if he insisted on raceriding again 48 hours later. The best-laid plans often go astray, however, and when the rider got a phone call on Saturday evening while getting gentle relief in the hotel's spa bath, he knew he had no choice but to drive the 178 miles back to Oxfordshire to ride several horses schooling over fences for his retaining trainer, who was totally unaware of his jockey's plight.

Padded like the Michelin man, Philip got through the Sunday morning session and also managed to raceride the next day. Can you imagine any other profession commanding such enthusiasm or dedication from its workforce? It must confirm what I've said before, that jump jockeys are quite mad.

Many of the surprise exits from races are funny when the bruises have subsided, with ego or pride the only things dented. What many regular race-goers fail to understand is the bond between horse and rider. The whole thing revolves around confidence from the saddle being transmitted to the horse. Occasionally a horse will over-rule a jockey's instruction, but in the main if a rider knows what he is doing and is definite with his commands, the horse will react willingly. When they argue or defy you trouble starts, but once you get to know their traits there is usually a way round them. In extreme cases, where a horse does the opposite to a command, reverse thinking – kidology if you like – works a treat. A good example of this came at Plumpton on a hard-mouthed, ignorant chaser whose recent form had promoted him to odds-on. Having won on two previous mounts that afternoon, I decided I was as good as a certainty for the headlines in the next day's *Sporting Life*, and it occurred to me that a good photo to boot would do my career no harm.

From the start he was intent on running away with me, so after one jump I let him have his head. This left him bewildered with no one to fight, and sure enough he dropped the bridle and lobbed along sensibly. Plumpton is a left-handed course, so when asked to rail tight into the back straight my gelding opted to hang badly right-handed out of sheer stubbornness. Instead of a fight I said okay and let him drift alarmingly close to the outside wing of the fence, which frightened him marginally more than it frightened me. Now an understanding had been reached. We would respect each other's skin.

The rest of the race went well, with a long gap to our nearest pursuers as we rounded the final turn into the short home run with just two fences to negotiate safely. Unusually the second last fence is an open ditch, which causes problems when there is a real battle, but ought to have posed none for me, well clear of any challenge.

Having set the horse up on a perfect stride pattern that would see us reach the take-off board without need for any last-second changes, I set about getting myself into a tidier position for the front-page photo. Head down, bottom up, tuck the elbows in, a quick glance at our shadow to check on the style, and we were into the last stride.

The horse had felt me relax as I attended to my vanity, was unsure now my commands had ceased, and instead of soaring over the jump, put in an extra stride which took him into the open ditch, smashing the guard rail and my game plan with it. There was a photo in the *Life* next day, to be sure, but it was not by any means the one I had been seeing in my mind's eye, and it served to remind me once again that pride *does* come before a fall.

Tregonwell Frampton – Father of the Turf

MILES NAPIER

The impressions of a visitor to Newmarket in the reign of Queen Anne were to be recorded some forty years later (whether at first or second hand is not clear) by a certain Dr Hawkesworth in issue no. 37 of the *Adventurer*.

> Being there in October, I had the opportunity to see the horse races, and a great concourse of nobility and gentry; but they were all so intent, so eager, so busy upon the sharping of the sport, their wagers, their bets, that to me they seemed just as so many horse-coursers in Smithfield, descending, the greatest of them from their high dignity and quality, to the picking one another's pockets and biting one another as much as possible, and that with so much eagerness as it might be said they acted without respect to faith, honour or good manners.
>
> There was Mr Frampton, the oldest, and as they say, the cunningest jockey in England; one day he lost 1000 guineas, the next day he won 2000, and so alternately. He made as light of throwing away £500 or £1000 as other men do of their pocket money, and was as perfectly calm, cheerful and unconcerned when he lost a thousand pounds as when he won it.

The 'cunningest jockey in England' was never a jockey in the modern sense of the word; that is to say he was never a professional racerider. The Newmarket visitor, however, was correct according to the terminology of the age. The original *Oxford Dictionary* defined a jockey as 'one who manages or has to do with horses'. Tregonwell Frampton admirably merited this description, since he was arguably more things to racing than any other man in history.

Frampton's role in the annals of the Turf is described as 'Keeper of the Royal Running Horses', a post which he held under four successive sovereigns (William III, Queen Anne, George I and George II). Precisely what his duties consisted of is uncertain: in all probability they were those of trainer-manager. If this supposition is correct, Frampton must go on record as the first person in history to train racehorses professionally. But the functions which he exercised in racing were not confined to training. He was called upon to adjudicate in many disputes both in relation to the running of horses and wagering upon them, thus constituting himself as embryo Jockey Club member. He would arrange matches and the terms on which they were to be run (functions which today would be performed by professional handicappers and race-planners). And in his penchant for dealing transactions there are parallels between Frampton and the modern bloodstock agent. It would not be far off the mark to describe him as the first 'Mr Racing'.

Tregonwell Frampton was born in 1641, the fifth son of William Frampton of Moreton, near Dorchester. The Frampton family had acquired the estate some three centuries earlier when a Walter de Frampton, of a family settled in Weymouth, married the heiress of the Manor of Moreton, Margaret, whose name is believed to have been Husee. The first member of the family to have achieved anything of note was Tregonwell's great uncle, Robert Frampton, High Sheriff of Dorset in the year of Queen Elizabeth I's accession, who built a Tudor manor house on the property. (This was to be pulled down some two centuries later.)

Frampton's Christian name was also the maiden name of his mother, whose family, likewise of Dorset origin, were the owners of Milton Abbey. The Tregonwells had a most interesting connection with racing. In the middle of the nineteenth century, Bruce Lowe completed his classifications of the lines of direct female descent in the thoroughbred. He discovered that the Natural Barb mare of Mr Tregonwell could claim the most winners of the Derby, Oaks and St Leger among her direct female line descendants. According to some racing historians this Mr Tregonwell was Frampton's maternal grandfather. Assuming this to be true, heredity is likely to have played a major part in shaping the destiny of the 'Father of the Turf'.

There is very little on record concerning Tregonwell Frampton's early life. It is not known whether he received any formal education;

whether he was destined for any specific profession; what relations existed between him and his family; what influences of heredity or environment led to a lifelong love of horses, greyhounds, hawks and gamecocks and to an equally enduring hatred of women.

The clearest details of Frampton's life begin to emerge from 1689, the year in which he went to live at Newmarket on a permanent basis. It has been suggested that he was involved in racing before that date, having horses in training at Newmarket and possibly holding a post of some description under Charles II. It is on record that on St Patrick's Day 1675, Frampton won heavily owing to the defeat of Lusty, a mare from the well-known stud of Lord Montague of Cowdray. The young gentleman from Dorset had engaged nine hundred pounds on the chances of his horse Nutmeg against Lord Montague's mare. Nutmeg had won as it had done in the previous year when raced against the Duke of Albemarle's Black Buttocks. In the next year Frampton ran a match for one thousand pounds against a horse belonging to Sir Robert Howard's son, a gamble which even the Duke of Devonshire, one of the most audacious plungers of the day, would have hesitated to take. In April 1680, Frampton's Race Mare was matched for three hundred guineas a side, half forfeit, against Mr Ashton's mare at Newmarket.

It seems likely that in his early years Frampton 'commuted' between Newmarket and his native West Country, his luggage being conveyed by a train of mules – no small undertaking in that age of appalling road conditions, rough weather and thieves of every description lying in wait for unsuspecting travellers.

An active follower of hawking in the west of England, Frampton had lived in a farmhouse at Waddock on the Moreton Estate. How as the fifth son he came to inherit the estate is a mystery; but shortly before his move to Newmarket we discover that, having sustained heavy gambling losses, he conveyed the Moreton estate to his cousin William.

In 1695 Frampton was appointed 'Keeper of the Royal Running Horses'. He was paid one thousand pounds a year 'for the maintenance of ten boys, their lodgings etc and for provisions of hay, oats, bread and all other necessities for ten racehorses'. He lived on the site of what is today Heath House, famous for its associations with the celebrated Victorian trainer Matthew Dawson but whose present incumbent is Sir Mark Prescott.

At this point in the story it is important to dispose of a very repugnant incident that was attributed to Frampton. It was alleged that he castrated the famous racehorse and equally famous sire Dragon, in order to qualify him to run in a match as a gelding. The evidence on which the story rests made a considerable stir at the time, but is now generally discredited. Frampton did own a horse by the name of Dragon; but this horse was racing some thirty years after the alleged incident took place. Mr J. B. Muir's book *Frampton and the Dragon* provides a masterly discussion on the subject and thoroughly negates the slur on Frampton's reputation.

Frampton's new role to begin with was primarily that of trainer. The Royal Stud was based at Hampton Court, under the management of Richard Marshall, and in all probability the pick of the Stud was sent to be trained at Frampton's stables. According to the practice of the time, Frampton would arrange matches between the horses of William III and those of such excellent sportsmen as Sidney Godolphin, the Duke of Devonshire, Lord Cutts, or Sir John Parsons who was twice Lord Mayor of London.

The stakes in these matches were high. Two thousand guineas was the sum involved in a match between the King and the Duke of Devonshire (the outcome of which is unknown). In a match for five hundred pounds, His Majesty's Turk defeated Lord Carlisle's Spot on a tight rein. Other good horses (either bred or imported) who ran for the King were Cricket, Cupid, Stiff Dick, The White Barb, Chillaby, the Black Barb (without a tongue) and Hutton's Gray Barb.

King William had adopted racing from the moment of his accession, although it is not known whether he did so for political reasons or for love of the sport. Whatever his motives he proved to be a great benefactor to racing and, by founding the Royal Stud at Hampton Court, he laid the foundations of the modern thoroughbred breeding industry. Less commendable was his insistence on enforcing the Act which prohibited all Catholics, on pain of death, from owning horses whose value exceeded five pounds; many of the old Catholic families had been great supporters of racing. Members of the Frampton family had come to the rescue of their Catholic neighbours, the Welds, who had become victims of the Act, by concealing their horses from the King's men.

Frampton's greatest passion outside racing was cockfighting – in which his royal employer took a keen interest. The King was present on 7 April 1698 to witness 'twenty-five cock matches between my Lord Ross and Mr Frampton at 5 guineas a match and for £500 the odd one'. Frampton won sixteen of the twenty-five matches and thereby £540.

When Queen Anne succeeded to the throne, she retained Frampton's services as a trainer, running many horses in his name as well as in her own. Frampton continued to 'match-make' for the royal horses. On one occasion, acting on the Queen's instructions, he issued a challenge to the Dukes of Devonshire, Rutland and Somerset to produce six horses to run against six of the Queen's, one hundred pounds on each horse. They were to run every seventh day until the six had been matched. It was further laid down that if one of Frampton's horses was 'out of order' another could be run twice. It is highly tantalizing that there is no record of the outcome of this intriguing contest!

If the outcome of the 'challenge to the three Dukes' remains a mystery, this is not the case with another affair in which Frampton was concerned, which gave rise to as complex a piece of malpractice as has ever been seen at Newmarket.

The 'Old Merlin' controversy is perhaps the best-known event in Frampton's life. Opinions are divided as to the year in which the event occurred, but Sir Theodore Cook is emphatic that it took place in 1704. Sir William Strickland, a Yorkshire baronet, owned a good horse called Old Merlin. Frampton made a match to run his 'favourite' horse (whose name is not recorded) against Old Merlin, the race to be run at Newmarket. The race, looked on as a great contest between North and South, attracted a great deal of interest and large sums of money were wagered on the outcome. A contemporary poet penned the following lines:

> Four and Twenty Yorkshire knights
> Came out of the North Countree
> And they came to Newmarket
> Mr Frampton's horses to see.

Frampton could be unscrupulous when it came to outwitting his opponents. Sir William had sent Old Merlin to Newmarket to be prepared for the match by Heseltine, a leading trainer of the day.

Frampton sent one of his grooms to Heseltine suggesting that if the rival horses were to run in a private trial previous to the match, at the weights and conditions agreed upon for the match itself, both partners would know the relative merits of each horse and could make a lot of money. Heseltine at first refused, but in a manner that suggested that he might in the end be won round.

As soon as the groom had left Heseltine sat down and wrote to his master to tell him what had taken place. In his reply Sir William urged Heseltine to accept Frampton's offer. At the same time, however, he instructed him secretly to make Old Merlin carry seven pounds more than the weight agreed upon, thus deceiving his rival as to the Yorkshire horse's true ability.

In the trial Old Merlin defeated Frampton's horse by a comfortable length. Frampton however was far from dejected. For he also had instructed his groom that his horse should carry seven pounds more than the agreed weight. He and his supporters had naturally concluded that since their horse had run Old Merlin to a length carrying (as they supposed) seven pounds more, he could not fail to beat the Northern horse on level terms.

In fact, of course, both horses, unknown to their opponents, had carried seven pounds overweight. So when the big day arrived and the North met the South the result was what might have been expected. Old Merlin won by about the same distance as in the secret trial.

At about this time, it is said as a result of the sums won and lost on the Old Merlin affair, a statute was enacted enjoining penalties on any person who should win ten pounds from any other person or persons. The effect of this statute was to make any race for a prize of over ten pounds illegal. There seems to have been no attempt to enforce this statute at Newmarket, but racing as a whole suffered badly. As breeders rightly maintained, what was the purpose of, at considerable expense, importing Arabs and trying to improve their bloodstock, to race for only ten pounds. This irrelevant statute was to be repealed in the reign of George II.

It was under the patronage of Queen Anne that Frampton began to take on the role of Turf Arbiter, which in the time of Charles II had always been undertaken by the sovereign. Racing was not at that time the well-organized sport that it is today. There was no book of rules to provide guidance, parliamentary legislation was at best intermittent and the influence of the Jockey Club would not be felt for another eighty years. In the absence of any governing body, a free-for-all atmosphere naturally prevailed. In the days of Charles II it had not been unusual for the King, his brother the Duke of York and their Lords-in-Waiting to take up their positions at a point towards the end of the course, and as soon as the field reached them to accompany them hell for leather to the winning post. Since order and procedure were virtually non-existent there was no alternative but to rely on the individual with the superior knowledge – in this instance Tregonwell Frampton – to pronounce judgement.

Queen Anne, like William III, was a great supporter of racing. The sport could have had no better friends than her and her husband Prince George of Denmark. During a visit to Newmarket by the couple in 1705, Anne ordered the rebuilding of Palace House, presented one thousand pounds towards paving the streets and endowed two charity schools. She and the Prince gave many plates and cups to be raced for, and they raced themselves. The Queen's greatest contribution to racing however was to stage a race for one hundred guineas 'to be run for on the New Heath at Ascot', thus laying the foundations of the Royal Meeting. She presented George with a racehorse called Leeds, which had cost one thousand guineas and herself raced the good horses Pepper, Mustard and Star.

Both William III, who spent much time in Frampton's company, and Anne had been true devotees of the sport. George I was not. He was more interested in his own court circle from Herrenhausen than in the racehorses of his adopted country and Frampton took advantage of the situation to do a good deal of racing on his own account.

Frampton never ceased to look for new outlets for his passion for gambling. Pond's *Kalendar* records two most curious matches which took place at Newmarket on 1 May 1724. The two matches were made by Tregonwell Frampton 'with his bigger and lesser mules against Mr Vane's grey Costly, for 100 guineas, 9 stone, 6 miles'. Costly won each match, but the entries in Mr Pond's publication need some explaining. This is afforded in Frampton's will, in which he excepted from a bequest of his horses 'a brown horse, called the Mule, nominated to be given by me to the Marquess of Blandford'.

Gambling was not the only way in which Frampton chose to augment his salary. He was at his most astute as a dealer. Although most of his deals involved exchanges, he liked to be sure of pocketing a little cash as well in case he came out the worst in the transaction. This was to the liking of the Earl of Bristol, the Master of the Horse, who was fond of a 'chop' as he termed it – although he had to part with some money to balance the transaction. Lord Bristol recorded in his diary a bargain between himself and Frampton. 'Paid him, for Mony, in Chop between a little grey nag of his and a grey mare of mine, £12. 18s. 0d.' Later he records 'Paid Mr fframpton in chopp between bey Jack and Dunn, £50.'

From the time that Frampton, at the age of thirty-four, made his first appearance at Newmarket, his opponents were left in no doubt that he was a force to be reckoned with. There were admittedly times when the Duke of Devonshire was too clever even for the wily west countryman. In 1698 and 1699, the Duke was given a verdict in the House of Commons by a jury against Frampton's claims 'in the matter of a horserace'. But in the long run it was the aristocratic plungers who lost. At the spring meeting of 1698, Lord Ross's Peacock had to pay forfeit at nine stone over six miles to Cricket, alternatively described as the King's and Mr Frampton's. Stiff Dick, another horse who answered this description, defeated Lord Wharton's Careless at the same meeting. Lord Ruthen received forfeit from Mr Frampton's Ball as the trainer had 'made better matches to be run next meeting'. Frampton's successes were legion, but he suffered his reverses. Dragon, one of his favourite horses, was to find one too good for him in the Duke of Bolton's bay Bolton.

For nearly fifty years Frampton dominated English racing. Yet no Turf historian has succeeded in giving his readers a true insight into the character of the man himself. Outwardly, Frampton impressed his contemporaries as eccentric. His style of dress (certainly in his later years) was uncouth; for three successive reigns he made no concessions to changes in fashion. Attired in this manner, he would make his way even to Court where he would enquire in a most off-hand way for his master or mistress, the King or Queen. Anne referred to him as Governor Frampton.

Perhaps the strongest clues to Frampton's character can be found in the works of art that portray the different phases of his life. The first portrait, painted by R. Pyle, depicts Frampton as a young man and is inscribed 'the founder of Newmarket racecourse'. The second, painted by John Wootton, was completed in middle age; the third painting, which was also the work of Wootton, was completed the year before Frampton's death. It shows him with a whip in his hand, a gamecock strutting on the table beside him and a greyhound resting its head on his knee.

In all three portraits the features are identical – the clean-shaven face, with firm lines about the mouth and chin and the strongly marked aquiline nose. Yet in all other ways the contrasts between the paintings could not be more pronounced.

Pyle's painting shows him as a fresh-complexioned young man, naive perhaps, but confident and self-assertive, and dressed (in striking contrast to his later years) in the height of fashion. The later portraits depict a very different person and opinions are sharply divided as to the true character of the subject. The middle of the three paintings of Frampton gave Bill Curling (formerly 'Hotspur' of the *Daily Telegraph*) the impression of a man who was 'hard and calculating'. John Hislop, the highly distinguished author and journalist, opined that Frampton was 'a tough, cunning, humorous and strong personality'.

Aubrey Noakes, the author of that well-written volume *Sportsmen in a Landscape* saw in the last of the paintings depicting Frampton 'a queer, wizen-faced fellow, ready to blackmail the lot of us'. Sir Theodore Cook is more charitable. He writes of 'the eyebrows that seem fixed in that gentle upward curve of politely tolerant amusement'. The strong conflict of opinions quoted above suggests that it must have been hard for Frampton's contemporaries to discover his innermost thoughts and feelings!

The puritan instinct which is present in so many of us causes us to suspect those who indulge in any form of heavy gambling. This is why the Corinthian scale of Frampton's wagering may cast doubts upon his character. But under no circumstances could he be saddled with that unattractive modern epithet 'compulsive gambler'. Frampton may have been intrepid in his wagering; but he possessed a cool and calculating brain. He sustained many heavy losses in the course of his career on the Turf; but he died a rich man.

Tregonwell Frampton had no sentimental ideas about sportsmanship. In modern terms, he could be described as 'sharp' (although he was not alone amongst his contemporaries in this respect). It would however be wrong to describe him as a man without honour or scruples. No person can have so great a success with horses as Frampton did without having a strong understanding of them; and the man who can get the best out of his animals is rarely a villain at heart. Had Frampton been a dishonest man, it is most unlikely that this trait would have gone undetected through four reigns. And Queen Anne must clearly have entertained a healthy respect for Frampton's knowledge and experience, or she would not have placed so much reliance upon his judgement in matters of dispute. His employers, who were in the best position to judge him, clearly thought highly of him.

Until nearly the end of his life Frampton continued to match his horses in Yorkshire as well as at Newmarket. It can be suggested that he was motivated by a desire to avenge the defeat of his favourite horse at the hands of the Northern-trained Old Merlin.

Although Frampton still held office at the outset of George II's reign, he was to be succeeded in his duties later that year by Thomas Panton, the father of 'Polite Tommy Panton', who was to win the Derby of 1786 with Noble.

Frampton died in 1729 at the age of eighty-eight. He was buried in the centre of the chancel of All Saints Church at Newmarket. In his will, Frampton left the bulk of his fortune to the second Earl of Godolphin. The features of the man who dominated Newmarket for so many years are on display on the walls of the National Horseracing Museum.

Tregonwell Frampton possessed none of the reforming zeal of such Jockey Club members as Sir Charles Bunbury, Lord George Bentinck and Admiral Rous. He was however the first person outside the royal family to exert a major influence on racing; he was without question the most versatile man in the entire history of the Turf; and he admirably filled the power vacuum which existed between the death of Charles II and the emergence of Jockey Club power. But perhaps the most striking feature about him was his complete individuality. Not the least intriguing aspect of the history of racing is the variety of the people involved. And the 'Father of the Turf' was, whatever else, a colourful personality.

The Ovaltinies

MIKE SEABROOK

You can stand in a pub anywhere in south-eastern England and say almost anything you like, and be pretty well guaranteed that no one will respond. However outrageous your remark, however factually incorrect, however it may ask, beg and pray to be corrected by those of superior knowledge, no one will say a word. There are, as far as my researches show, only two ways to jolt these strange people out of their shrouds of reserve and shyness. One is to light a cigarette in any location whatsoever where it is prohibited, and the other is to speak in praise of horseracing. This is absolutely certain to bring forth a torrent of wise sayings like 'you don't see many bookies in bus queues', or something similarly profound.

And yet, damn it, I *like* racing. And betting. Yes, I do. I enjoy putting a few bob on a horse. Not fanatically, in either case. I'm not a racing lunatic, or a freak. There are many things I like more than horseracing: books, my microscope, cricket; music and writing sure as hell I like more. And the same with betting: I'm not, never have been and never shall be a candidate for membership of Gamblers' Anonymous. I've never plonked the housekeeping or next month's mortgage on some three-legged cripple that couldn't win if everything else in the race developed spavins or the botts a hundred yards from the winning post. No. I enjoy just what I said I enjoyed: putting a few bob on a horse, now and again. When I've put it on I regard it as money spent, not invested, so I don't mind if I lose, and I'm as chuffed as hell if I win – and very agreeably surprised as well.

As far as this aspect of racing goes – the betting on it, I mean – I am a net loser. Of course I am. The sententious prat in the pub who reminds you that you don't see many bookies in bus queues is quite right, as far as fact goes. Of course most people who like a bet now and then are losers. I've had to stand and let this be pointed out to me umpteen times in the course of my life, and what I've always wanted to ask at the end of it is, so what? Sometimes I have asked this, and every time it evinces the same result: a kind of puzzled, blank stare, as if you've asked some colossally important but totally, theologically unanswerable question about the nature of the universe, such as 'where are you when you've reached the end of the universe – what's outside it?' or 'if everything was created in the Big Bang, what was it created *in*?' These people who take it upon themselves to lecture you on the futility, immorality and fundamental wickedness of betting on horses look at you with just that vague expression of surprise, as if you've committed some appalling breach of etiquette – which, actually, you have; because what they really feel, you can see from their smug expressions as they deliver their little homily, is that they shouldn't have to justify their point of view. Racing is immoral and betting on it is even more immoral, and that is a fact that comes straight from God, so just who do you think you are to be asking them to justify it?

So then, as I say, overall I'm not ahead of the bookies; and I very rarely believe any man who tells me he is. But I say again, so what? Every man has the right to go to hell in his own way, and if his chosen way is putting too much money on the horses, that's his right. If his wife starts going without the housekeeping and the kids start starving, then it becomes something very different, and he deserves all the kicks, poverty, guilt, divorce and misery he gets out of it, but none of that makes the slightest difference to his initial right to go to hell as stated. Besides, all that happens to very few people. Most are like me: they put a few bob on now and again, and come to no harm. In return they get excitement, the fun of anticipation, and occasionally a vast, warm, surging glow of pleasure at getting something for nothing. And if it isn't really for nothing at all, that's what it feels like at the time, so why should any miserable-gutted killjoy feel it necessary to come self-righteously along pointing the fact out and pricking your little bubble of mildly self-delusive pleasure? They wouldn't take the same evident delight from telling five year olds that Father Christmas doesn't exist, would they?

No, they wouldn't, and the reason is not far to seek. They wouldn't feel jealous of the five year olds, whereas they do feel jealous of you when you've just come reeling out of the betting shop clutching your sheaf of lovely, greasy used tenners and twenty quid notes. There's no feeling quite like taking money off a bookie, and none that quite matches it, and they know it, because they can see it, written all over your face. The beer you buy with bookies' money always tastes that bit better than beer you buy with your own.

Talking of gambling, I have known one man who really was a member, at one time, of Gamblers' Anonymous. His membership had long since lapsed by the time I came to know him, but the problem still existed. We both worked in the same industrial estate in Hemel Hempstead, and were both in the habit of going for a liquid lunch in the very pleasant bar of the local squash club every working day. We would talk racing most days – not all; once again, there was a moderation about it that anti-racing fanatics seem to find difficult to credit in anything to do with racing. And every Thursday we both used to take the afternoon off.

Promptly at ten to one a cab would arrive, and we would drain our beer, say unusually bright and cheerful cheerios to one and all, and off we would go. The cab would take us to a pub called the Golden Cockerel, which had a very unsavoury reputation, but was in fact a very agreeable place, run by a towering, genial and very funny ex-bodyguard to a famous pop group.

There we would drink with that huge extra pleasure that always attends drinking when one ought by rights to be at work. The first pint never touched the sides. The second was down by ten past one and then, the keen edge taken off our thirst, we would sip the third as we pored over the *Sporting Life* (bought by each of us alternately every Thursday on the way into work in the morning) making our selections for the afternoon.

By twenty past we would have picked our principal horses for the day, and we would trot over the road to Jennings, the local bookmaker, and on would go the bets – mine coming to a total of two or three quid, his to twenty or thirty. He would always have something in the first race, so we'd wait listening to the blower for the result. Then we would go back to the Cockerel, our mood elated or subdued according to the way his first selection had fared.

After that I wouldn't generally see him for several hours. What usually used to happen was that at the official closing time of 3.00

John would go across the road to Jennings, to spend the remainder
of the afternoon in serious betting, while I stayed in the pub for a
game of cards. Then, at 5.30, when the ex-bodyguard could resume
serving openly as hard as he had been serving clandestinely all
afternoon, John would reappear. Occasionally – very occasionally
– he would be wreathed in smiles and strewing money. Most times
he would slip through the door, glancing about him as if on the
lookout for policemen, sidle up to me or some other acquaintance,
and ask sheepishly if he could scrounge a pint. His friends would
then keep him moderately in beer until the following pay-day, when
the cycle would start once more.

His wife eventually tired of his regular disposal this way of his
entire wages, and somehow got him committed to one of the local
mental hospitals. He spent several months there and got out to find
that she had secured a whole sheaf of court orders and injunctions,
awarding their house and possessions to her and ordering him on
pain of mediaeval penalties to keep away from it, them and her,
and requiring his employers meanwhile to reserve a sizeable portion
of his wages thereafter for her, before he ever got the chance to
lay hands on it. He was a new man after that, light of heart and
gay of countenance. He still lost what remained of his wages every
week, but he had also lost the feelings of intense, racking guilt that
accompanied the procedure, and his new abandon was a tonic to
witness.

I got a great deal of pleasure out of John over the few years of
our close acquaintance, before I moved from Hemel Hempstead
and the industrial estate and on to brighter things. He had a happy
way with an utterly inconsequential turn of phrase, which used to
convulse me at times. Like many people, he had a pet adjective:
'Let's go and have a profound bet,' he would say; and we had many
a profound pint together. On one occasion he announced that all
his horses had lost. 'Och!' he cried at the conclusion of the sad tale,
'we'll be murdered in our beds!' Another time he delighted me by
informing me, in thanks for some service – standing him a pint, I
dare say, after he had lost his shirt on some broken-down hack that
couldn't lose if it tried – that I was a scholar and several gentlemen.
Once, when the racing was off and John, I and several others had
repaired to my house for an afternoon of cards, attended by some
pretty heavy drinking, he rang for a taxi to take him home. There

was a crackle from the other end, upon which he snorted indignantly, 'What the fuck's it got to do with you where to?'

As I said, I share with John the fact of being permanently behind the bookies in my betting. But I did win sometimes; it is perhaps a testimony to the rarity of this event that I can remember, with gratitude, the names of many of the horses that obliged for me. Sea Pigeon was a fine, sterling old horse, who had transferred to the jumps as he got too old for dashing along on the flat, and he won money for me on half a dozen occasions, possibly consecutively. Two other reliable old warhorses I remember with great affection were Burma Pink, another former flat horse turned jumper, and Pink Blues, who had one of the fleetest turns of foot I ever saw.

Lord Howard de Walden's classic miler Kris won a fortune for me, as did a wonderful animal called No Bombs, who won several races and looked likely to become very big indeed until one fateful day when he took a fancy to a Mars bar being eaten by his lad in the horsebox en route to a meeting somewhere up north. He pinched the Mars bar literally out of the lad's hand and guzzled it in a single bite, arrived at his meeting, won his race by several miles, and was promptly disqualified for failing a dope test straight afterwards. It turned out that the Mars bar was to blame, containing traces of several substances severely prohibited by the Jockey Club; but I never got my money back. Incidentally, Kris, as well as winning a considerable sum for me on the racecourse, won a considerable amount more off it, in bets on the meaning and pronunciation of his name. (A kris is a small Malayan dagger; it is pronounced like the boy's name, Chris. Most people seemed to have a strange urge to call him Crease.)

But of all the bets I ever made, I think the most satisfying was the small fortune I cleaned up on Troy in the Derby in 1970-something – still, to my mind, the most electrifying race I ever did see: head waiter tactics from Carson in about seventh place until everyone (including me, twitching spastically and ruing the half-drunk state in which I had allowed John to talk me into betting approximately ten times the largest bet I ever, otherwise, placed in my life on the creature) was certain he'd left it too late. Then a lightning, deft little sidestep to get him through a momentary gap that looked too small for the jockey, let alone the horse; but through it he went, like a rat up a drainpipe, and then the most glorious, thundering finish to storm home like an armoured column, accelerating smoothly away from the rest as if they were standing still.

I also cherish the memory of the two occasions when I did something many punters never achieve even once in a lifetime of betting: all four up in a yankee. Strictly I ought to claim this distinction once only, because the second time I actually had three winners and a non-runner; but the first time it was genuine enough. I can't remember the horses, but oddly enough I can remember the odds, and the exact sum I collected from Jennings, over the road from the Cockerel. They came in at 11/4 on, 5/4 on, 7/2 and 6/1, which saved the day, and my humble 10p yankee (tax paid) put a marginally less humble £27.28 in my credit balance. I had enormous fun over the next few days, calculating what I might have won if I'd backed all the outsiders I quickly convinced myself that I'd nearly backed, instead of the pair of odds-on favourites.

In terms of odds, though, nothing could compare with the horse that came in third at 50/1 with a fiver of my money riding on it each way, or my own great coincidence double. I was playing kaluki in the Cockerel, as I did every Saturday from opening time at 10.30 until closing at 3 p.m. It was an odd school, because of the other players Bill, the landlord and former minder, was ten years older than me, and the rest of the school were all old boys of sixty-plus, much given to singing 'We are the Ovaltinies' in chorus as they played their cards and swigged their beer. We all bet on the horses, so every Saturday, at 12.30 sharp, the hand in progress was completed, then an interlude was called. Pint pots were replenished, papers were opened to the racing pages, and a deep and intense silence would fall over the table. Gradually a few comments would be made, to be greeted with ribald and derisive ripostes concerning the previous speaker's ideas of what might, what could and what might not, could not and would not as long as it had a hole up its posterior, win the such and such at so and so.

Eventually all the selections were made, Jennings slips were produced and completed, and it then fell to me, as the youngest by thirty years, to take them (illegally), along with the money (even more illegally), and run across the road to the betting shop and place the bets. The times I glanced at their selections as I waited to cross the road, saw what a motley assortment of donkeys they had chosen, and thought, shall I or shan't I . . . ? I often used to cross that road with upwards of a hundred pounds in my hand, and it would have been so easy to start off a promising career as a bookmaker that I was often very nearly fatally tempted. In the end I never did it, because of simple lack of bottle. The one day I decided to hang on to their money, I always used to think to myself, some cripple would come in for sure at a 100/1 or something, and I'd not only be bankrupt for the rest of my life as I paid out on easy terms, but I'd have blown my reputation into the bargain. So I never did. And as far as I remember, on the occasions when I was tempted to hang on to the money and hope the donkeys all lost, they always did, every bloody one of them.

However, on this Saturday morning, I had picked half a dozen out for my usual bet (two threesomes, doubled and trebled up), and was idly browsing through the cards to see what else was running when from between the pages of the *Daily Mirror* belonging to Charlie Lloyd, one of the circle of assiduous students of form, there emerged a large and splendidly coloured spider. Everyone spotted it except Charlie, and the predictable remarks about his wallet were duly made, scoffed at and forgotten. Meanwhile I went hastening back to the racing pages, where I was sure I had spotted something . . . and I had. There it was, running in the 4.10 – odd how I can remember the time of the race, but have no recollection whatever of the course on which it was being run. But there, at all events, was the name, as large as life: The Spider Man. And the price – 16/1, no less. I'd never backed a winner at better than tens in my life. I had to have five bob on this, I thought. And as I closed the paper and reached for a slip from the heap on the table, my eye was caught by another entry: in another late race, somewhere else, there was a runner I had backed – successfully, at that – once or twice already, by the name of The Vinegar Man. And he was marked up at 14/1. I did some rapid mental arithmetic, and worked out that a five bob each way double would net me no less than £67.74 if they both won. I clutched a slip and scribbled as if my life depended on it. The others all saw me doing it and asked curiously what I was up to. The moment they knew, of course, they all did the same, and Jennings went down by huge sums that day.

Eventually I moved away from the area, and have never been

back to the Golden Cockerel since. But I had a vast amount of fun there, and all of it was closely bound up with racing and betting. I miss the old crowd, though I doubt if they are still assembling on Saturday mornings. Some of them are dead, I guess; some will have moved on. But if any of them are left, I have no doubt they are still opening their papers at the racing page at 12.30 on a Saturday morning, wherever they are. I hope they've found someone to run to the bookie's for them.

As for me, I still watch the racing on the box whenever I happen to be watching and there's racing to be seen, and it still exercises the same attraction. I like the bright colours, the atmosphere of noise, excitement and tension. I like the crowds; they seem to me to be some of the most uninhibitedly cheerful crowds to be seen at any sporting event. There are few sporting crowds more visibly intent on enjoying themselves – and as Stevenson acutely observed, there is no duty we so much underrate as the duty of being happy. I still, as I always did, prefer the flat to the jumps, I don't know why. On the face of it the jumps has far more excitement. But there seems somehow to be more pure drama in the flat: the contest is more visible, the tension greater.

It's an odd predilection, taken all round – especially considering that I can't ride and that nothing on earth would induce me to go within biting or kicking distance of a horse, let alone attempt to sit on its back. I am a devout follower of Ian Fleming's ideas on the horse: an animal dangerous at both ends. But that doesn't stop me from being able to see and appreciate the beauty, power and grace of horses of the racing variety. When Desert Orchid gracefully accepts a sugar lump and nibbles it fastidiously between his front teeth, or old Red Rum opens yet another betting shop and seems to be quite palpably enjoying himself, I can feel really very fond of them – which, coming from a notable non-animal-lover like me is quite an accolade. And even now, fifteen years after the event, I still get a shiver down my spine when I think of Troy's sudden, electrifying acceleration to warp factor five to win that Derby, or recall how I felt as I watched old Rummy win his third Grand National; Kris's devastating turn of speed, or Pink Blues turning it on one evening at Goodwood to win me all the money I'd lost in the course of a whole bad month; valiant old Sea Pigeon, his great heart still as good as gold, pounding over fences to win goodish races at thirteen or so; Captain Christie, the very first horse that ever won money for me, storming home in the Cheltenham Gold Cup with all my hopes, and a hideously high proportion of my month's salary, riding on his broad back. They're good memories, all of them, bringing back excitement almost without a parallel in any other form of entertainment; and whatever may be said by puritans and self-righteous prigs, it's a good, clean, wholesome entertainment, at that.

The Start of My Career

PETER WALWYN

So many people, when writing their life stories, are inclined to say that details of their childhood are tedious. I disagree – what fun I had, even as a rather lonely boy, during the Second World War, the only son of elderly parents, who were almost too old to have the sort of fun and games that normal children have with their parents. Don't get me wrong, they were very kind and protective, to the extent that I might have been described as being rather precious.

When my father retired from the army just after I was born we lived in a lovely rambly Cotswold-stone house in Gloucestershire, with hunters, grooms and 30 acres of ridge and furrow old grass fields round us. The first recollections of sport I have are of sitting on my beautiful pony Kitty Brown and being taken by my nanny on a leading rein down to the nearest covert being drawn by Percy Durno, the huntsman of the Heythrop hounds; it was near Evenlode, and was called Hutchinsons' Folly, after a famous hunt secretary.

My father till he died always prided himself in the fact that he had never paid more than £300 for a horse, and he made very few mistakes, on buying horses or dealing in them. He had been brought up in the Monmouthshire country, where his father had retired, after serving in India at the time of the Mutiny, and had seen action at the second relief of Lucknow under Sir Colin Campbell. I still have in my dressing room his campaign mirror, which would have needed at least two bearers to carry it.

My father had run away from Wellington College to join the volunteers in the Boer War, commanded the riding troop at Woolwich, fought in the Great War in the Royal Horse Artillery, and commanded 'E' battery when it fired the first two shots in the First

Great War. He had also been a great show-jumper and military rider, riding several winners at Punchestown before the First World War, and representing army teams in competitions in New York, Chicago, Paris and San Sebastián in Spain, as well as winning the Grand Military Steeplechase at Sandown, just after the First World War. He was described by Tom Masson, a great trainer and top show rider, as having 'hands like velvet'.

At some stage, having been severely wounded and been given an MC and DSO, he got as far into the War Office as a mere major dared tread, and told the Director of Cavalry that in his opinion 'the standard of riding in the mounted regiments is quite appalling'.

He suggested that the cavalry training school at Netheravon and the artillery school at Woolwich should merge, and that furthermore he should be the first chief instructor. To his amazement these wishes were transformed into reality, and he was brought back from France before the cessation of hostilities to formulate the new combined school at Weedon in Northamptonshire.

This was the nucleus of all military riding, and it is still carried on at Melton Mowbray, where the riding courses provide students with three horses to ride and look after: a made horse, a half-made horse and an unbroken horse. The young soldiers were all encouraged to go hunting whenever possible, but poodle-faking was not approved of; if it were done it had to be done in spare time, and with the proviso that they were back in barracks before reveille.

I was allowed a four-ten shotgun at an early age, and was soon crawling about and stalking rabbits with my spaniel at my heels until nightfall, and lugging handfuls of dead rabbits home, while my parents were yelling from the terrace that supper was ready.

This is the sort of life we led in the holidays, with hunting with the Heythrop in the winter holidays, in the war-years, when the pack was run on a shoe-string but of course was essential to keep the foxes down. Prep school was near Hindhead, but I was never any sort of scholar, and even worse at games. It was a nice school, though, with lots of reasonable friends, and I managed to squeeze through my common entrance to Charterhouse.

Charterhouse was very different. There were and are very few people there from the same sporting background, and certainly, unlike so many other public schools, no pack of beagles. However, I survived long enough to get seven ordinary levels in School

Certificate, and became a house monitor. Then it was a question of being called up for National Service. I had, according to the doctors, a bad back, which has never bothered me until this day, but any thought of getting a commission was totally ruled out.

I was therefore posted to the Intelligence Corps depot near Uckfield. On passing out in field security, I was sent to Klagenfurt in Austria, where I spent a lovely year, ending up as a corporal, wearing civilian clothes most of the time, because I spoke German, and being driven round in an unmarked car all over the province of Carinthia.

Of course, all the time I hankered after living a country life, and having been spurred on by the exploits of my hero and first cousin, Fulke Walwyn, the leading amateur rider of his day and then leading National Hunt trainer, I wanted to try and become a racehorse trainer. My parents, or more probably my mother, were horrified at the thought – all booze and betting – but when I insisted I was set on it they did everything they could to get me the right grounding.

This consisted of an interview with a very well respected and successful flat-race trainer at Newmarket, Geoffrey Brooke, the introduction being done by a great friend of my father, Geoffrey Freer, the senior Jockey Club handicapper.

Mr Brooke accepted me and I embarked on three of the most formative years of my life. For the first year I had no car, only a bicycle, but, starting off doing my two horses and then progressing under the guidance of a wonderful head lad, Bob Ruttle, I started to learn my craft. After a few weeks I was promoted to head lad in the bottom yard, a collection of ramshackle buildings at the bottom of the big paddock, with a sea of mud in front of the boxes, and a lot of wild Irish apprentices under me.

I learnt very quickly to feed horses, and some of those under my care were little two years olds, who had to be coaxed to eat anything at all in the daytime, as they were being put through their paces to no mean tune, in order to exploit their modest capabilities.

Geoffrey Brooke was a wonderful trainer, especially of the two year olds and they were always ready to win first time. He and his wife Betty were kindness itself, and underneath a rather bluff exterior there was a heart of gold.

My bottom yard succeeded in having seven winners before the

top yard had got going, but of course we had the precocious horses and it wasn't long before animals were being swopped around, and I was sent the horses with problems, while my pride and joys were being ridden up to the more prestigious and important top yard, which was much more amenable to the owners. In most cases they were personal friends of the 'Guvnor' and I couldn't have met a more delightful lot of people.

Gradually the bottom yard was transformed with mown lawns and rose beds, and it was time for promotion. After a year without a single outing in charge of a horse to the races, Bob Ruttle suggested I travelled the horses to the second meetings, which I gladly took over. Sometimes by train, from the old station and usually by British Railways or Hammonds horse boxes. The train journeys were most fascinating, with a lorry picking up all the food and clothing for the horses, and the horses themselves being led down to the old station one and a half miles away, usually in pitch dark, along the walking ground beside one set of gallops.

What would have happened if a horse had got loose I dread to think, but all was well, and I can't remember this happening even once. The train usually consisted of what was called a 'special', with its own engine, a carriage for the travelling head lads and a guard's van on the back.

Horses always travelled well that way, as the guard's van gave the convoy stability, and the horses weren't swayed about as they were on the roads of those days. Until the motorways came along this was by far the best way of travel and horses seemed to run better and keep their form.

After two more years of travelling horses all round the country, in the summer I was able to slip away for a short holiday and hunting with my parents; it was then a question of where my future lay. My grounding had been impeccable, with me now being able to do most jobs in the yard, except one I can't do to this day, plaiting a horse's tail. This is very seldom done in flat race stables and I am against plaiting manes for racehorses, as a well pulled mane looks just as good as a plaited one, using in so many cases elastic bands instead of thread, and usually far too many plaits. Bob Ruttle had taught me so much. He was the most extraordinary little man, weighing under seven stone. He would ride anything and used the most fractious filly as his hack, setting off each horse of a string of thirty in turn at the bottom of the canter without a care in the world, though he was over fifty, and as fit as a flea. When not in the yard with his horses, he was mending rugs and doing odd jobs, to smarten the place up and save money for the 'Guvnor'.

Although my lodgings were not always the best, the hospitality I received at the Brookes' nullified that, as I always had breakfast in the house, usually rushed, sometimes after leading a horse home for two miles from racecourse side, our stables being on the other side of town. My appetite was rapacious, and there was always a mountain of delicious fry-ups, which other guests, staying in the house or there to see their horses work, had left behind, and there was often a dinner party to which one was asked, as a spare man. At these one just sat and listened as the great and famous aired their views on racing.

I was then suddenly approached by my first cousin, Helen Johnson Houghton, to hold the trainer's licence for her, at Blewbury in Berkshire. She had started training when her husband Gordon had been so tragically killed in a hunting accident in 1951. He was the most promising trainer of his era, and was held in high esteem, although I sadly never met him.

At that time women were not allowed to hold a licence to train horses, and so, although the real trainer was the woman, either head men or assistant trainers were allocated a licence. I didn't know her at all well, but her reputation as a horse-master was legendary, as was her very short fuse. I was probably lucky but we had four very happy years together, and I considered her a genius in placing horses as well as being an excellent judge – and very little was missed in her evening stable inspections.

When I arrived, there were only twenty ordinary horses, except for the moody Gilles de Retz, who had won the 2000 Guineas the year before but was not certain to show his form in each race he ran, although he was a very good horse on his day. I gradually learned the intricacies of organizing the galloping grounds, of mole catching, and so many facets of running a stable, and learning Helen's art of placing horses.

At the end of four more very happy years, during which the stable extended to eighty bulging boxes, I felt that, having met the most glorious girl, it was time to dip my toe in the water and try the art of training myself. I had no offers of horses, but my parents had sadly died the year before and I had a small inheritance.

We married in the spring of 1960, and that autumn we found a small stable to start from. This was Windsor House in Lambourn, a Georgian house, two cottages including a hostel and thirty boxes. It had always been a lucky yard, first with Sir Charles Nugent and his grandson Hugh, and then with Fred Rimell's father Tom, and latterly with Sid Mercer, the cunning old fox who had started his career with Tom Coulthwaite, the trainer of three Grand National winners at Hednesford. Sid's ability extended to curing warts, and he certainly fixed some I had on my hands with a lick from his tongue on to a far from clean hand which he wiped on my own.

Having bought the stable for the then considerable sum of £12,000, it was our job to try and fill it. The first person to offer me a horse was Percival Williams, then Master of the Four Burrow hounds in Cornwall. He had his wife's home also, in Herefordshire, where he kept two mares. One was Aunt May, bought with a legacy left him by an aunt of that name. We were asked over to Herefordshire by him and his heavenly wife, Barbara, in pouring rain, to see Aunt May's first foal. I remember well going into a field on a hill where there was this insignificant yearling gelding by Roc de Diable. When Percival waved his handkerchief, the little horse did stretch out his toe, and he could certainly move.

Having accepted him to train, we drove away, and I said to my wife that at least we ought to be able to train him well, as it was the only horse I was likely to be offered!

Little did we know then that he would eventually win twenty-seven races, including at Deauville, ridden by Lester Piggott, and at St Cloud. He eventually broke a hind leg, cantering at home when he was fourteen, having beaten the winner of that year's Royal Hunt Cup at Ascot, a month later at Brighton. Sadly he had to be destroyed, which was a tragedy that I felt especially keenly, as he and Mr Williams had started us on our career.

Also in the yard at that time was a lovely gelding by Mossborough called Don Verde. He was a liver chesnut of the loveliest colour with good limbs. His owners, Captain Philip Dunne and his son Martin, had had him in training with Syd Mercer and he had run once with promise over hurdles. They asked me if I would keep him on, and he certainly seemed a reasonable prospect.

When we moved into the yard, there had been a fair amount of neglect, and even in the house there was no heating of any sort. However, by rectifying that and renovating the shabby lads' hostel, we soon got the place more tidy.

The other asset we took over was Syd Mercer's head lad, Ray Laing. He was a brilliant feeder and adept at breaking in the yearlings, and was the backbone of the yard for seventeen years, until he decided that the pressures of an expanding yard were too much for him, although he had very good back-up from the other head lads that I recruited, as time went by.

Until a young person starts training, it is impossible to appreciate the difference in running one's own show, and that all the decisions now lie with you. However much help you give to someone else, whether your advice is taken or not, now the ultimate decision lies with you. Where you run, who rides, whether the horse is fit enough or has been schooled enough are the result of so much thinking, which no one else can do for you. Our first runner was a shallow little horse called Port Stride in a handicap on the flat at Warwick, and he finished second to our amazement and delight.

We decided to run Don Verde in a novice hurdle at Worcester on 22 October, and John Oaksey, who had qualified at the Bar but then suddenly decided that race-riding and journalism were much more to his liking, had been down to school him and he seemed a natural jumper. In the race he was always handy, jumped well bar the second last hurdle, and drew away easily to win by eight lengths. The amazement was unbelievable: actually to be able to train a winner with my second runner was incredible. Although we have had over 1800 winners since, in England, Scotland, Ireland, France, Italy, Germany and the USA, the feeling of having one's name in the paper the next day was amazing.

So many people are involved in the preparation of a horse that I always think it unfair when only the trainer's name appears, as it is only thanks to the hard work of a *team* that results occur. Even the youngest apprentice is partly responsible and how proud he must feel too that all our efforts are coming to fruition.

I still have my first wages bill, a total of four employees and £19. 18s. 2d. This shows you what successive bad governments and inflation have done to our economy. Very few people in this country are any better off than in those days.

When anyone starts training, even with the massive backing that

I never had, it is hard to believe that one is capable of training top class horses, which after all is the real purpose of the exercise. That is the fascination of being a racehorse trainer, being totally immersed in one of the most all-embracing and absorbing occupations that was ever invented.

A Cautionary Tale

PAUL HAIGH

Well, why not a stretch limo?

Somebody might as well ride in them now they've been built. And besides, if lapsed old socialists of the champagne variety are going to boycott them, what's going to happen to all those good, honest, horny-handed sons of toil down at the Mercedes stretch limo factory?

That was what we wanted to know.

We didn't take a lot of self-persuasion. After a minute or two it was in a mood of something like self-righteousness that we reclined on the seats behind Brian, the driver. After a mile or two we were stretching our legs over the small ballroom between us and him, and wondering why the hell he wasn't wearing his peaked cap. By the time we got to Dublin we were practising Queen Mother-style waves at startled members of the public, who, to our delight, instead of giving V signs back, looked guiltily at each other as though they knew they really ought to, but couldn't quite remember who we were. So, auspiciously, began the freeby of freebies: the 1994 Bord Failte (Irish Tourist Board) expedition of drunken (I speak only of myself here, just in case any of the other bastards is thinking of contacting a libel lawyer) British racing hacks to Punchestown for the annual jump racing festival. There were five of us altogether. The others were Alistair Down (*Sporting Life*, Channel 4), Ian Carnaby (*Sporting Life*, *Irish Field*, Sky TV), and Cornelius Lysaght (BBC Radio), who at Eton used to sit next to Darius Guppy, the friend of royalty and jewel thief. That's three. At Punchestown we were joined by Sir Clement Freud who, perhaps wisely, believes in travelling alone.

This is a cautionary tale, and like all cautionary tales it begins on a note of optimism. If you have tears, prepare to shed them.

Irish hospitality is serious, and this time the Bord Failte was serious too. A decision had been taken at the highest level (believed to be Charlie Macreavey, Minister of Tourism himself, or perhaps even at the United Nations in New York) that Punchestown's April meeting is to be promoted as the third leg of a jumping Triple Crown – the first two legs of which are, of course, Cheltenham and Aintree – and the kindness which the Bord, through Maire, our delightful hostess, lavished upon us was merely an implementation of this important policy shift.

Treating people like royalty is rather wasted on royalty because they get treated like that all the time. Racing hacks have a different perspective on life and its vicissitudes. Some of us can remember walking home seven miles in West Australian heat from a race meeting at which we have done our rail fare. Some of us can remember gluing down the soles of our shoes in the lavatory at Ammanford bus station after a similar bit of folly in South Wales. Most of us can remember the hospitality at Fontwell in the old days when the fare in the press room consisted of a cup of tea – and a slice of seed cake if the turnstiles happened to have been clicking; or at Devon and Exeter, as it was then called, where, for disciplinary reasons, the clerk of the course had denied scribblers refreshment of any sort for four years after John Oaksey had made some careless remark within his earshot about the angle of the curl of the slice of Mother's Shame on the lettuce sandwiches.

We had, in short, as the now-bald old hippy James Taylor once put it, known sunshine and we had known rain, and on the whole the rain had tended to predominate. Stretch limos were not wasted on us, nor was drink, nor was the Westbury Hotel when we finally got there later that first, disturbing night.

First, though, we were whisked (have you ever been whisked?) from the airport to the course in a state of high excitement and Brian's car. Lily was waiting for us.

There are two things you have to remember about going racing in Ireland. You are considered extremely eccentric if, when you arrive, you don't buy a Turform [sic] racecard for three pounds and a sprig of something lucky for about the same price. You are considered even more eccentric if, when you leave, you do not buy several bars of chocolate and large quantities of pears. For some reason it is taken as axiomatic that no sane person could wish either to enter or leave the course without supplying themselves with these commodities. Lily has the concession. Confidently she approached us with shamrock and Turform as we arrived. Maybe our big mistake was to turn her down.

Have you ever been to a three-day, twenty-one-race meeting at which you failed to back a single winner? It is tempting to describe it as a sobering experience, but in this case the phrase would be inappropriate.

Armed with Lily's Turform and a shamrock we might just have stood a chance. Burdened with hubris, and vanity about our good fortune in being invited – the stretch limo didn't help – we never had a prayer.

Lunch in Ireland is always something of a euphemism. Lunch at the Punchestown Festival, splendid in the extreme though the food in the Festival Marquee turned out to be, is the sort of experience that breaks backs. 'Now,' say the Irish decisively. 'What will you have to drink?'

You muse a bit. You put on the old show: 'Oh, well, I don't know. Shouldn't really drink when you're punting, you know, ha, ha.'

And then when you have told them and the drink is brought, they place it in front of you with the word 'Now' again on their lips, only this time with expectancy and a hint of command, with a hint too of an implication of complete confidence that the serious business of the day has *now* begun.

It has. It had.

Lunch was the only time we had available in which to study the form. The *Racing Post* had printed it, but only for a couple of races. The *Sporting Life*, which was in the process of moving its offices from Holborn to Canary Wharf – this isn't a bit of axe-grinding: this was their excuse – printed the next day's card. Or maybe it was the day after that's. It's hard to remember exactly, although it could not, of course, have been the day before's. In any case it was no use, and even if it had been it wouldn't have mattered. We had no opportunity for conventional studying. We were having lunch.

What's more, we had the diversion of Clement Freud to contend with.

Clement, as everybody knows, is a gourmet. And a dogfood specialist. And a wit. And a columnist for various newspapers as well as the *Sporting Life*. He is also a former amateur rider, an ex-MP, the grandson of the founder of analysis, the brother of a famous painter, the father of Emma and, when it comes to matters of service and cuisine, more than a bit of a martinet.

He wasn't staying with us. It may not be quite true but a rumour was going round that the only hotel he'll stay at in the east of Ireland is the Keadeen at Newbridge, because the Keadeen is the only place he's stayed in often enough to have trained the staff.

We were very impressed by the Festival Marquee. Clement is a hard man to impress. 'Is there any chance of some butter?' he asked coolly as he examined a pile of individually wrapped Kerrygold.

There was a lot of that sort of thing, and to our general astonishment it all worked. Nothing was too good for 'Sir Clement'. If Sir Clement disliked having his butter wrapped in tinfoil – an entirely understandable dislike, we all agreed, by the way – then carefully moulded pats of unwrapped would be provided for him.

The lunch was a buffet. When Sir Clement announced that he hadn't queued for anything since the overthrow of the late Führer, and did not intend to resume the practice now, a waitress materialized to fetch his salmon and assorted seafood. When he frowned in distaste at the appearance of a piece of ham on his plate, she hastened away to remove the offending object.

Astounded by his aplomb, his chutzpah and his *savoir faire*, we picked at our own solids between heavy gulps of alternative nourishment. Meanwhile Clement, who had just celebrated his seventieth birthday by hiring a first-class train to take a large party of friends to Ludlow racecourse, entertained us with his skills as a limericist. He had a fund of them and they were all pretty good. He seemed relatively unimpressed, however, by my own contribution, which went as follows:

> There was a young man named Frank,
> Who never quite mastered the wank.
> His elbow gyrated,
> His pupils dilated,
> But it never inflated: it shrank.

Whether because he felt it lacked pornographic depth or because he doubted my claim to have concocted this epic while still an undergraduate, his bloodhound eyes glazed over as I clapped my hands in a positive ecstasy of self-approval, and with a mere three minutes to go before the first, he suggested that we should now consider our investments.

At Clement's instigation we all put money into a pool for the jackpot. It definitely wasn't Clement's fault that it failed to survive the first leg. It was fate. It was all preordained. It was just a hint of what was to come.

Irish bookmakers have a way with drunks and optimists, and they have a special way with drunken optimists from across the water. They know you're in possession of a self-destructive impulse that badly needs to be fed, and they understand. They really do. They know you are there to drink yourself stupid and then do what is left of your brains on the horses, and so they try to make life easier for you.

In England it is really quite difficult, unless you are a major compulsive with totally atrophied judgement, to back more than one or two losers per race. In Ireland it is very difficult to restrain yourself from backing four, or even five. Irish bookies bet without the fav. They bet without the fav and the second fav. Some of them bet without the fav and the second fav and the third fav, and without a couple of outsiders too – just to give you the impression that for betting purposes your horse is about the only one left in the race.

This is invariably *almost* true, but not, of course, quite. It is simply axiomatic that if you back, say, the third favourite without the front two in the betting, it will indeed be beaten by the front two. It will also lead over the last, run out of steam on the run in, and be caught by the only one in the field which was running for the bookie. It doesn't matter how many horses you exclude, somehow yours gets done.

This hurts.

Never mind. Anaesthetic is available in the Marquee. Another glass of it and you are ready to repeat the process on the next race.

How bad did it get? Well, let me put it this way. By the end of the first day all the money which had been hard won from Victor Chandler over the winter through a careful campaign of abstemiousness and selective investment that culminated in a winning (!)

Cheltenham only a few weeks before, had gone. Not some of it, all of it. Four months' work down the drain.

Square one threw a welcome home party.

Whether it was as bad for the others is hard to say. But in Brian's car on the way back we were considerably more subdued than we had been as we'd left the airport. There were a few whimsical remarks about our conveyance having the turning circle of the Torrey Canyon, and suggestions that we should all be equipped with loudhailers so we could communicate with Maire in the front passenger seat. But on the whole they lacked conviction and were delivered with a decided absence of panache.

We stopped at a pub called the Johnstown Inn, where a small band was playing – presumably in our honour since there didn't seem to be anyone else about, and no one was really expected until later – and swopped stories about punts: mostly big punts that had gone wrong.

After we'd run through the afternoon's *angst* I told them my best horror story, about the $1400 I'd put on Dancing Brave for a place in the 1986 Breeders' Cup (in which he'd finished fourth) and sat back waiting for gasps and commiseration. But they seemed about as impressed as Clement had been by the limerick.

I soon found out why. The $1400 had been the biggest bet I'd ever placed in my life, and its loss, combined with the downfall of my hero, had left me speechless throughout a subsequent seven-hour session in a bar called the Drinkers' Hall of Fame in Arcadia, California. The others, however, bet like that if not as a matter of course then at least as a matter of occasional habit. Cornelius had gone home. Clement had gone off to a restaurant whose chef didn't fill him with fear and loathing. But Alastair had some tooth-grinding incidents to recall. Then Ian told us how he'd got so far into the hole on one occasion that he'd wound up having £6600 at 8/11 on a horse called Duggan *in a claimer* at Brighton. That shut us all up.

The fact that Duggan won was neither here nor there. We gazed at Ian with new respect. We were looking at a man who'd had his head in the mouth and smelt the breath of the beast.

Three or four introspective Jamesons with the proprietor later, while the band played Kenny Rogers's 'The Gambler' as we left, we were back in our conveyance, with Brian eyeing us warily in the rear view mirror.

That night we went to dine at a Dublin restaurant called Frère Jacques. After a few more drinks I began to speak in tongues. I remember some lobster arriving, but after that nothing, though I am reliably informed that the rest was not silence.

Only a punter can know what it's like to wake up in a strange room with a hideous hangover and try to work out how much damage you did to your bank balance the day before. Scraping together every available physical and mental resource, I managed to get Alastair on the room-to-room to ask how I'd got home and how high I'd scored on the ****ometer between the arrival of the lobster and the cessation of hostilities. 'Oh, around 6.5. I've seen worse,' he replied airily – but not specifically.

I told him I'd thought about it and decided not to go out to the course for the second day. I had some work to do. It was on TV anyway. So was Ascot, and besides . . . It wasn't necessary to go on. Alastair is the sort of man who's capable of understanding every dismal nuance of the phrase 'morning after'.

Nightmares deepen. It is not in their nature to take turns for the better.

In the back of my mind had been the demented thought that if I stayed behind and bet shrewdly on the phone I'd almost certainly get back the monstrous amounts I'd lost and more. Stay away from the booze. Stay away from the hospitality. Make sure you've got no one to talk to. All will be well.

Nightmares, as I say, deepen. The Wednesday was a great deal more grisly than the Tuesday had been. All day I lay quivering on my litter at the Westbury, the phones between Room 207 and Victor Chandler so hot they must have smoked. And the consequence was rout on a scale undreamed of. Patents, doubles, singles, each way. They all bit the dust so deeply there were toothmarks on the rock underneath.

At 7.30, by which time I had endured the slightly surreal experience of having several losers introduced to me by a Sky TV team that included Ian himself who had returned to Cheltenham for the express purpose, I decided to get out with one big bet. The horse was Lynch Law. He led over the last, went a length clear and was then caught on the line by a horse ridden by Adrian Maguire. Gibbering softly, I fell into a taxi and joined the others at a barbecue in a place called Swan Dowling's. The steaks were great. They tasted like sawdust.

In vain did I pull the usual stunt of persuading myself how lucky I was. 'Look,' I said to everyone, 'if we were proper journalists we'd be in a ditch in Sarajevo getting our balls shot off by hairy Serbs.'

It was true. But it didn't work. Self-pity's always at least 2/1 on to beat reason. This time reason never got it off the bridle for a moment.

Day Three of the punting equivalent of the Gallipoli landings. Day Three was so appalling it defies description. Day Three was the day on which with grim-jawed defiance we went straight back in on the drink to give us courage and then decided we were definitely – this time – going to get it all back. Somewhere around four o'clock one of us had a winner. I think it was £2 each way on a horse called Ultra Flutter. Apart from that the carnage was absolute. As we left the course even Lily, seeing the expressions on our faces, forbore to offer us the normally mandatory two dozen pears and four Twix for a pound.

In the car on the way back to the airport our depleted, defeated little band was now an object of friendly amusement to Brian. He'd had big-wig politicians in the back of his van. He'd had pop stars. God, he might even have had the winners of the Eurovision Song Contest whose contestants had taken over the hotel like representatives of a New Order as we'd checked out that morning. He'd never been impressed by us. Now he obviously felt pity.

He even laughed politely at our jokes. 'We hate people with short wheelbases,' we mouthed pathetically at motorists who drew level with us at the lights. 'Oh look,' we shouted hopelessly, 'stubby cars!'

As we approached the airport somebody pointed out to him that next time we wanted a lavatory on this hotel on wheels; considering the amount we were ingesting the absence of one just wasn't good enough. 'Oh dear,' said Alastair, 'do you mean there isn't one? I thought . . . I am most frightfully sorry.'

We were desperate. We laughed like drains.

You don't need to know that the plane was late because of a mechanical defect. You don't need to know we got into another session in the airport bar. You don't need to know things got even worse before they got better.

I told you this was a cautionary tale. Here are the cautions. Ireland is a beautiful country and Punchestown is a great meeting. But do not expect to enjoy both hospitality and racing.

There is no such thing as a free lunch. In racing there is no such thing as a free trip. Much later I worked out that the 'freebie' cost about the same as a month-long family holiday to Australia would have done. One day I will finish paying for it. In the meantime I've given up stretch limos for good.

Notes on the Contributors

GEE ARMYTAGE is a member of one of the most prominent racing families, and the leading woman jockey of her day. Among her achievements, she is the only woman yet to have won a professional race at the Cheltenham Festival meeting, has been the leading jockey at Huntingdon, has won many awards, including those of *Daily Telegraph* Jockey of the Year and Piper Champagne Horseman of the Year, and has been the leading woman National Hunt rider in England five times to date.

DAVID BENEDICTUS is a prolific novelist and author-director of plays for stage, radio, TV and cinema. His first novel, *The Fourth of June*, was a best-selling public-school story, and his second, *You're a Big Boy Now*, was made into a film by no less than Francis Ford Coppola. He was for five years until recently head of Readings for BBC Radio, where he was responsible among other things for the long-running *Book at Bedtime* series. He has been an active member of Amnesty International since 1963, chairing his local Amnesty group for fifteen years. In addition to being a life-long racing addict, he has devised a system for picking winners – though he still works for his living.

JOHN BUDDEN was a schoolmaster for twenty-five years. It was during that period that he began giving race-track commentaries as a hobby. He went full-time in the mid-1980s, and now commentates regularly, mostly on the northern circuit. He is also a regular contributor to the *Sporting Life*, writing features and a weekly column on 'The View from the North', as well as track reports. He was for many years the racing correspondent of the *Cumberland News*, and is 'Borderer's Gossip' in the *Racing and Foot-*

ball Outlook. He has also contributed to numerous books on racing. He is perhaps most celebrated for his appearances from time to time in the memoirs of his old friend and another of our contributors, Simon Raven.

MICHAEL CHURCH is Special Projects Manager at the *Racing Post*, and the author of numerous works on racing pedigree, including: *Dams of Classic Winners 1777–1993, The Classic Pedigree 1776–1989, Three Centuries of Leading Sires 1721–1987, The Magnificent Seven* pedigree charts, *The Two Thousand Guineas Chart* and *The Derby Chart*.

PAUL HAIGH writes regularly for *Racing Post* and the *Sunday Telegraph*, has written a book on leading trainers and contributed to numerous anthologies on racing. He was Racing Journalist of the Year for 1993. His life history spans four universities and three marriages, one of them to a Kentucky millionairess. Since they felt that he could not possibly declare to her father his true occupation, which was selling ice cream from a van, she suggested that he claim to be a racing journalist, a line that they felt would go down well in Kentucky. He then felt he had better try to turn the story into truth, and began from there.

TIM HEALD is a journalist and author of more than twenty books, from a series of crime novels to biographies of Prince Charles, the Duke of Edinburgh, Barbara Cartland and Denis Compton, by way of books on great estates, cricket and other varied matters. He is co-ordinator of the PEN International Writers in Prison committee, a former Chairman of the Crime Writers' Association, and a passionate but bad player of real, or royal, tennis.

TONY MORRIS has been a writer on racing and the breeding of racehorses for more than thirty years. He is the author, co-author or editor of numerous books and correspondent for numerous periodicals in Europe, America and Australia. He is currently freelance, contracted as bloodstock correspondent of the *Racing Post*. He is a Council Member of the Thoroughbred Breeders' Association since 1990, and in that year also was voted Racing Journalist of the Year.

JAMES MORTON is a solicitor by profession, who now devotes himself mainly to writing. His numerous books include a history of bent coppers, a study of London's criminal gangs, a biography of 'Nipper' Read and a dictionary of criminal argot. He also edits the weekly magazine for the legal profession, the *New Law Journal*, and contributes regularly to *Police Review* and other newspapers and magazines.

MILES NAPIER is a former handicapper under Jockey Club and National Hunt Rules and a regular lecturer on racing. In addition to contributing regularly to the *Irish Field*, the *South African Racehorse & Horseman* and *Owner-Breeder*, he is the author of *Thoroughbred Pedigrees Simplified*, *Breeding a Racehorse*, *Blood Will Tell* and *The Racing Men of TV*, and co-author with Leon Rasmussen of *Treasures of the Bloodstock Breeders' Review*.

ROBIN OAKLEY is Political Editor of the BBC and was previously Political Editor of *The Times*. (Before that, Assistant Editor successively of the *Sunday Express*, *Now!* magazine and the *Daily Mail*.) A lifetime racing enthusiast, he once used to write a racing column and stable features for the *Liverpool Daily Post* under the *nom de plume* of Mandarin. He lives in Epsom and never backs locally trained horses, which blow as heavily as he does jogging on the Downs.

GEOFF O'HARA was a bookmaker for thirty years. In retirement he writes short stories in which he chronicles the adventures of a bunch of more or less disreputable but likable characters to be found haunting one of London's less fashionable betting shops. Many of the stories appeared in the *Sporting Life*, and several have been read by the author on his local radio station.

EAMONN PERCIVAL was for many years a regular feature writer for *Sounds*, *Record Mirror* and *International Musician*, and has edited magazines on topics as varied as model railways, films and videos and CB radio. He also worked betweenwhiles in the computer industry. There he chanced to meet Mike Seabrook, and came thus to encounter many of the most prominent low life of

Hemel Hempstead. His knowledge of racing among other things was picked up from them.

RICHARD PITMAN dropped into horse racing after failing all nine 'O' Levels at Tewkesbury Grammar School in 1959. After fifteen years of galloping on and bouncing off the turf as a National Hunt jockey, he joined the BBC as a Paddock commentator. Since then he has written for many and varied papers, and has written seven books: an autobiography, three novels, two Guinness Steeplechase Guides, and a biography of champion trainer Martin Pipe. With his wife Mandy he owns a small stud in Oxfordshire and enjoys hunting with the Old Berks Hunt.

MICHAEL POPE was always interested in racing. While awaiting his return to England after the war he trained the regiment's racehorses, assisted by his brother Barry and Major Dick Hern. He started to train in 1947, managing studs for Lord McAlpine and Lord Strathalmond. In 1973 he retired from training on medical advice. He became President of the National Trainers' Federation and represented them on the Horseracing Advisory Council and other Industry committees until his retirement in 1988. He has written regularly for the *Sporting Life*, which published his recollections, *All Such Fun*, in 1993.

WILLIAM POWELL is a barrister by profession, and has been Conservative Member of Parliament for Corby, in Northamptonshire, since 1983. He has served on numerous Parliamentary committees, including long service on the All-Party Racing Committee, one of the busiest of all, and arguably the one with the most enthusiastic membership. As befits a member of this committee, he is a lifelong racing enthusiast.

SIMON RAVEN is among the finest contemporary British novelists and writers of *belles lettres*. As storyteller he has always been drawn to the ghost story, and his ventures into the genre have produced some of the most chilling and gruesome examples in contemporary letters. Meanwhile in his volumes of memoirs he has issued a series of sardonic, hilarious and often ferocious commentaries on the state of the nation and his own fortunes – which have depended, as often as not, on the abilities, antics and foibles of racehorses, most of them, alas, slow ones.

MIKE SEABROOK trained as a lawyer before running away to be a policeman. When he was tired of that he worked briefly as an advertising copywriter, and then served a ten-year sentence as a technical author in computers before going over the wall again, this time to be a full-time author. He is the author of four novels, the only wholly truthful book ever written in Britain about being a policeman, and a biography of the composer Peter Maxwell Davies. He has also edited a series of anthologies of new writing on sport, of which this is the latest.

JOHN TIMPSON has been one of Britain's best-loved radio personalities for many years. He started as a journalist in East Anglia, where he now lives, but spent most of his life as a journalist with the BBC. For some years he held one of the most prestigious positions in radio as chairman and question-master of *Any Questions*, but he is almost certainly still best remembered as joint anchorman, first with Jack de Manio and then with the late Brian Redhead, of Radio 4's flagship breakfast-time current affairs programme, *Today*. He is the author of many books, of which the latest is *Timpson's Timepaths*, tracing ancient routes from the Icknield Way to the Wey and Arun Canal.

IAN WALLACE was for many years one of Britain's most eminent operatic singers, singing many leading baritone roles. Since his retirement from singing he has made a second career as a radio and television personality, being especially well-known and liked for his genial contributions to the long-running series *My Music*. He is also an all-round sportsman, with a passionate interest in cricket and golf, rugby and association football and, of course, racing.

PETER WALWYN grew up with horses, and was determined from his childhood to work with them. He began as a pupil with Geoffrey Brooke, then went to assist his cousin, Helen Johnson Houghton – paradoxically holding her licence for her, since in those days a woman was not allowed to hold a licence! He began training on his own in 1960, and has been one of our most illustrious trainers ever since. He has trained winners in Britain, Ireland, Germany, France, Italy and the USA, and was Champion Trainer both at home and in Ireland in 1974 and 1975. The latter year was his *annus mirabilis*: he trained the Derby winner, Grundy, and also won the Irish Derby and 2000 Guineas, and the King George VI and Queen Elizabeth Diamond Stakes. He is currently Chairman of the Lambourn Trainers' Association.

REG WHITEHEAD has for several years had a special interest in fostering friendly relations between the British and Russian racing fraternities. He has been British team manager in several of the now regular annual Russo-British racing challenge meetings, including the inaugural competition, which he describes in this book. He is also Gee Armytage's uncle, and wearing his other hat acts as her manager and agent.

JULIAN WILSON has been BBC TV Racing Correspondent for twenty-nine years. As well as editing and presenting prestige programmes on Royal Ascot and the Cheltenham Festival, he has commentated on twenty-four Grand Nationals. He has also enjoyed success as an owner (notably with Tumbledownwind, Gimcrack Stakes, 1977), a breeder and racing manager. His books include the best-selling *Lester Piggott. The Pictorial Biography*, *100 Greatest Racehorses*, and *The Racing World*.